YES, AIDS AGAIN

A handbook for teachers

Hilary Dixon

Yes, AIDS Again

LD 722

ISBN 1 85503 168 X

© Text Hilary Dixon

© Illustrations Simon Barnes

All rights reserved

First published 1993

LDA, Duke Street, Wisbech, Cambs, PE 13 2AE

●●● *Contents*

●●●

Section 1 *'It's Nothing To Do With Me'*

Thinking About The Issues

INTRODUCTION

CLASSROOM ACTIVITIES
 · Word Association
 · Four Corners
 · How Would It Be...?
 · Risk Takers
 · What If?

Section 2 *'Not AIDS Again!'*

Understanding the Facts

INTRODUCTION

INFORMATION ABOUT HIV AND AIDS

STATISTICS ON HIV AND AIDS

CLASSROOM ACTIVITIES
 · Graffiti Sheets
 · Risk Card Game
 · Quizzes
 · What is Safer Sex?
 · Safe or Not?

Section 3 *'My Mother Said...'*

What I Have Been Taught about Myself and Other People

INTRODUCTION

CLASSROOM ACTIVITIES
 · Feeling Good About Myself
 · Messages, Messages
 · Valuing My Body, Valuing Me
 · Values, Achievements and Goals
 · Appreciations

Section 4 *'It Won't Happen To Me'*

Protecting Myself and Others

INTRODUCTION

SOME INFORMATION ABOUT SEXUAL BEHAVIOUR

CLASSROOM ACTIVITIES
- What Options Are There?
- What Do I Want?
- 100 Ways with a Condom
- Assertive Through and Through
- Asserting Myself

Section 5 *'They've Brought It on Themselves...'*

Challenging Prejudice and Discrimination

INTRODUCTION

CLASSROOM ACTIVITIES
- Story Lines
- Carpark
- Who Gets the Treatment?
- Media Messages
- Language Speaks

Section 6 *'What Can I Do?'*

Supporting People Affected By HIV and AIDS

INTRODUCTION

CLASSROOM ACTIVITIES
- Peter is HIV Positive
- Feel, Think, Do
- Feelings about Loss
- Helping Others
- Learning to Listen

Resources

Useful Addresses

Background Reading on HIV/AIDS and Related Issues

Training and Preparation for the Teacher

Materials for Use in the Classroom

••• *Acknowledgements*

This book has been a long time coming. I first recognised a need for it while working in the AIDS Education Unit of the Cambridge AIDS Programme. We developed close links with the local education authority and ran several courses and workshops for teachers. Out of these grew a Health Education Support Group which met a couple of times a year for mutual support and sharing of experience and ideas. Several valuable exercises and activities were created or trialled at these meetings. I believed they not only deserved to be published more widely, but that if they worked in schools in Cambridgeshire then they were likely to be useful to teachers in other parts of the country. It took the announcement that AIDS education was to be compulsory in schools from September 1992 to get a firm proposal together for a book. This is the outcome.

I want to acknowledge the people whose combined experience, creativity and willingness to experiment have contributed to this book. Thank you to all the teachers I have worked with over the years who have shared their experience, helped me develop my thinking and sometimes pushed me to re-evaluate; to colleagues from the FPA, some of whom started me on this path and others who supported, challenged and encouraged me over the years; to colleagues in Cambridge whose enthusiasm, energy and commitment enabled closed doors to open, new ground to be walked on and inter-agency partnerships to form.

It is often not possible to trace the lineage of a particular exercise, but there are some exercises used here which can be attributed to particular people. Specific thank yous are due to the unknown participants on an FPA course some years ago who devised 'Carpark', which was developed by David Dawson, and now seems to be appearing in training manuals everywhere; to Mike Fitzsimmons for 'Word Association'; to Maureen Binstead and her colleagues at Melbourn Village College who must have been among the first to take on the broader implications of AIDS in their teaching, and were particularly responsible for adapting 'Who Gets the Treatment?' for the classroom and writing 'How Would It Be...?'; and to Martin Johnson who devised 'Peter is HIV Positive' for a course for Cambridge University medical students.

Special thanks to Ruth Joyce who has encouraged me throughout the last few years, but particularly for her thoughtful and thorough comments on the first draft of this book; to Dr Chris Carne and Martin Jones of Clinic 1A at Addenbrookes who checked the section on factual information – and helped me to maintain accuracy whilst avoiding medical terminology; to Colleen McLaughlin who, in five minutes, moved on my thinking about evaluation; to Rodney Tyler who helped to track down newspaper headlines and articles; and to Jo Wroe at LDA whose belief in the product got me started and kept me at it.

•••

●●● *Introduction*

AIDS EDUCATION IN SCHOOLS

AIDS education has had a place in the curriculum of many secondary schools since the mid 1980s, most commonly in Science or in a Personal, Social and Health Education programme. Approaches have varied: many schools have had one-off talks to two hundred in the hall by a local GP, or incorporated a single lesson on AIDS into Biology; a few have introduced a carefully planned module into their existing sex education. Some governing bodies have made explicit reference to AIDS in their sex education policies, others have assumed teachers would use their own judgement and have provided little guidance. In a few schools there has been no AIDS education at all.

In September 1992 AIDS education became a compulsory element of National Curriculum Science in Key Stage 3. As a result, parents will not be able to withdraw their children from it, regardless of the policy of the governing body. For schools which are already including a thorough AIDS education programme, the recent changes will make little difference. However for others it is a major step, and may well be causing some anxiety, particularly where there has been no history of including health or sex education in the curriculum.

There is widespread concern – from government, professional and voluntary agencies – about young people's sexual behaviour, and a recognition that education must seek not only to provide information, but also to effect behaviour change among those at risk of HIV infection. In practice, the AIDS education provided by many schools is approached from a medical/biological perspective, and those who are now being forced into including it in the curriculum will be tempted to take this approach too. It relies on scientific data, is non-controversial and can be taught using traditional teaching skills. There is a danger that it will be 'ticked off' at the end of Key Stage 3 without it having made one jot of difference to HIV prevention.

It is important to appreciate that young people may have difficulty identifying personally with factual information when it bears little relationship to what they know and have experienced within their own lives. Research evidence clearly indicates that this form of AIDS education has no impact on young people's attitudes or behaviour nor does it support them to make good decisions. If pupils are to be encouraged to take control of their lives, then teachers will have to be brave enough to experiment with other more radical approaches. Schools have the opportunity to make a valuable contribution to HIV prevention work and to the future health and happiness of their pupils.

1

ABOUT THE HANDBOOK

This handbook is for teachers. It is intended to help those of you who believe you have some responsibility for the personal and social aspects of your students' lives as well as for their academic development. It provides opportunities for making AIDS education relevant and useful. It gives clear information; encourages exploration of the way in which HIV may impinge on young people's lives and those of others; and helps young people to develop the skills to put what they know into practice.

AIDS education cannot and should not be value-free. The values implicit in this book are respect for self and others, equal opportunities and freedom from prejudice, exploitation and fear. The materials work towards helping young people develop high self esteem, good communication and caring relationships. The style is one of exploration, discussion and empowerment, in which each young person is encouraged to develop his or her own value system and make good decisions based on it. Your role as teacher is to facilitate, support, challenge and inform, and by example, to demonstrate the value of self esteem, and respect for self and others.

The handbook aims to support those of you who work in key stages 3 and 4, with students from 11 to 16/18. It is appropriate for those of you who are teaching the compulsory elements of AIDS education in National Curriculum Science and for those who are raising AIDS education as part of a broader Personal, Social and Health Education programme. It provides background information, resources and practical activities for those who are anxious about teaching this subject, and offers some new perspectives and material for those who are already competent and confident.

CONTEXT FOR AIDS EDUCATION

AIDS education should not be taught in isolation; it must be set in the context of the broader issues. There is no one right place for it in the curriculum – in fact it could be argued that *where* is far less important than *how*. A look through this handbook illustrates its link with the study of infection and disease, personal and social development, sexual health, communication skills, prejudice and discrimination and community care. It is hoped that although the focus of the book is AIDS education, it will be used to foster links with other areas of the curriculum.

●●● *Preparation and Planning*

TEACHER PREPARATION

It is vital, in an area as sensitive and personal as this, that you are thoroughly prepared. If you are new to AIDS education you will find it helpful to read through the handbook to familiarise yourself with the issues, approaches and material. Reference is made in the text and in the resources section at the end to further sources of information and background reading. I particularly recommend Clift and Stears' 'AIDS : The Secondary Scene' as a companion to this handbook.

You will need to familiarise yourself with –

• *legislation and guidance on sex education and AIDS education (see pages 16–18)*
• *the programmes of study and attainment targets in the relevant curriculum areas*
• *your school sex education policy to ensure that what you propose to teach is consistent with it*
• *any guidelines from your local authority which may provide you with additional support and encouragement.*

There are several courses offered around the country to prepare teachers for teaching Personal, Social and Health Education, Sex Education or specifically AIDS Education, particularly the FPA, Brook Advisory Centres and TACADE. Local Education Authority Advisers and Health Authority Health Promotion Units may also run workshops or be willing to offer support.

You might also consider forming a small support group among colleagues. It will not only enable you to share experience and develop ideas together, but will also provide a safe place where you can talk difficulties through in confidence. You may well find that as you develop skills in this area of work, so young people bring their problems to you – it cannot be overemphasised how important it is to have support for yourself when this happens.

DEVELOPING A PROGRAMME

You will need to decide your purpose, or aims and objectives, for teaching AIDS education and select appropriate activities. You will also need, however, to consider the ability, maturity and knowledge level of the group, the level of trust and your own competence and comfort. It would be unwise to attempt any of the exercises in this book without first taking time to think them through carefully, considering some of the issues, questions or difficulties that could arise. If you have a support group of colleagues this is an ideal place to try out exercises.

PURPOSE
Each exercise includes the following information:

AGE GROUP
This is to enable you to identify exercises that will help you achieve your aims and objectives.

LEVEL
Each exercise gives some indication of the age range for which it may be suitable.

You will need to be aware of the level of trust and the level of knowledge and awareness in a group when planning which exercises you might use. The guidance under this heading will help you to decide whether a particular exercise is appropriate. If you are working with a group over a period of time, the level of trust is likely to increase. The first grading will indicate how early on you might use the exercise. If you are likely to be working with a group only for a few sessions, you will need to consider whether to use any exercises beyond those graded 'does not require high level of trust in group'. The second grading will help you to order a programme by starting with exercises that 'require no pre-knowledge or understanding', and gradually developing to those which need 'considerable pre-knowledge and understanding'. Throughout there is an assumption that students come into school with some beliefs about HIV and AIDS.

TIME NEEDED
This is a rough guide to how long an exercise will take and whether it is possible or appropriate to split it over two or more sessions.

MATERIALS
Most activities and exercises in the handbook need very few materials. Preparation will be eased if a flipchart or blackboard, large pieces of paper, felt tip pens, A4 paper and pens are available at all lessons. Additional materials required for an exercise will be clearly indicated under this heading.

METHOD

This is a step-by-step guide to setting up and running the exercise, including variations and possible follow-up.

REVIEW

This is included on those exercises which do not flow directly into another exercise, and provides an opportunity for students to consider what they have learnt and apply that learning to other situations.

It is important to remember that students, teachers, schools and contexts vary widely. What is appropriate when selected by a particular teacher for a group in one school may not be appropriate with another teacher, another class, in another school. You will have to decide an appropriate programme for your situation. This book does not attempt to lay down what you *should* do, but rather what you *could* do.

CLASSROOM ENVIRONMENT

In an ideal world you would probably choose to work with small groups in a comfortable relaxing room with the chairs arranged informally in a circle. Such an opportunity is rare in secondary schools, so compromise is essential. If you can, request a room which allows flexibility – the space to arrange the chairs in a variety of ways, a place to write, the opportunity to make some noise without disturbing others, wall space to display material and, above all, privacy.

If students are not used to working experientially, it may take some time to develop sufficient confidence and trust in the group, and between the teacher and the group, to enable some of the exercises to take place. It will also be important to consider carefully whether the atmosphere is likely to be conducive to sensitive discussion or whether it could fuel prejudice and discrimination.

One way of developing trust, which many teachers are now using successfully, is the group contract or ground rules (see page 6). This is a set of behaviours drawn up and agreed by the group. They are there to help students feel safe enough to explore issues, and will normally include reference to issues such as listening, respect, confidentiality and not putting people down. In this context they might also include being non-judgmental and not making assumptions about people.

GROUP RULES

Confidentiality
Don't laugh at others
Listen to one another
No teasing
Don't be afraid to speak
Be honest
Respect others' feelings

A teacher cannot guarantee absolute confidentiality to an individual or a group. It may be helpful to explain that you will not gossip with colleagues or parents about anything that has gone on in the sessions, that you are available to talk privately with pupils and that there may be rare occasions when you are told something by a student which must be passed on. If this situation arises you will probably first want to explain why you have to tell someone else, and then ask the student's permission. There should never be a reason to pass information on without the student's knowledge.

Students also need help in handling confidentiality. It is one thing to agree it, another to cope with knowing a secret and the pressure to tell. Some discussion of what confidentiality means and strategies for handling it will be useful. It also needs to be clear that pupils are under no pressure to reveal information about themselves or their families. They must judge levels of trust in the group and take responsibility for what they choose to tell. This may be an issue for you too.

STUDENTS' EXPERIENCES

It is important that you recognise the variety of experience in the classroom, and do not make assumptions about students. There may be students who already identify themselves as lesbian or gay, or who are confused about their sexual orientation; students who are – or have been – sexually active and those who are not; students who have been pregnant, had an abortion or are parents; those who have been abused or exploited sexually, or maybe who abuse or exploit; and those who have experimented with drugs, legal or illegal. Others may have experience of these issues in their family, among friends or in the neighbourhood. You need to be aware of these differences; where appropriate, you may use them in the classroom; but above all be careful not make assumptions that will cut off learning for individuals or groups of students.

If you assume that no students are sexually active, there is a danger that those who are will see the lesson as irrelevant and a confirmation that teachers are out of touch; they may also be unable to ask the questions for fear of revealing themselves. If you assume that all are sexually active, you give no validation to those who are not yet ready, have not yet had the opportunity or have decided to wait, and you add to the pressures that are already all around them. A similar argument could be used regarding assumptions about drug use. If your language is explicitly or implicitly heterosexist, you run the risk not only of marginalising students who are lesbian or gay, but also of confirming for them possible feelings of isolation, abnormality or invisibility.

It is important not to make assumptions about cultural or religious groups either. There may be as much variety in the beliefs of any one religious or cultural group represented in your classroom as there would be between different religious or cultural groups. Several books and pamphlets have been written on this subject but there is no substitute for meeting parents – asking them their views, listening to their responses and engaging in a dialogue with them.

GROUP SIZE

You will be very lucky indeed to have the opportunity to work with a group of eight to twelve students. The reality is that you are more likely to have a class of thirty. There are ways to handle this number without teaching didactically, and most of the exercises in this book can be used successfully with large groups.

Individual work of course is not new to teachers. It can be used to start pupils thinking about an issue; or for reflection and writing down private thoughts and feelings.

Small group work is often under-utilised in schools. It is a way of involving all students in a task by giving them an opportunity to share knowledge, experience and skills. It may be less threatening than whole class discussion and less isolating than individual work. The number in the group will be significant. For some sensitive issues two or three people may be sufficient, and it may not be appropriate to ask for feedback. For most tasks a group between four and eight will be best. If a group gets larger than this some students may find it hard to get involved.

Whole class discussion can also be useful, generally in order to hear what small groups have been doing or to review a section of work. If it is for reporting back it needs to be well structured and crisp, otherwise groups may find it hard to concentrate (see the section on Discussion on page 14).

EVALUATION

Evaluation is important, not least because educational establishments are being asked to account for what they do and to demonstrate their effectiveness. Despite the fact that it is notoriously difficult to evaluate the impact of a health education intervention on knowledge, attitudes or behaviour, and formal research methods are unrealistic for most teachers, you will need to make some kind of an assessment of whether your teaching has been successful. Below is a strategy for attempting classroom evaluation.

First, start with a clear set of aims and objectives for each session and for the programme as a whole. Without these it will be difficult to know what you are trying to assess.

Second, provide an opportunity for students to review their learning as part of the exercises. This book uses experiential – or participative – methods, which take account of the experiential learning cycle (see next page).

EXPERIENTIAL LEARNING CYCLE

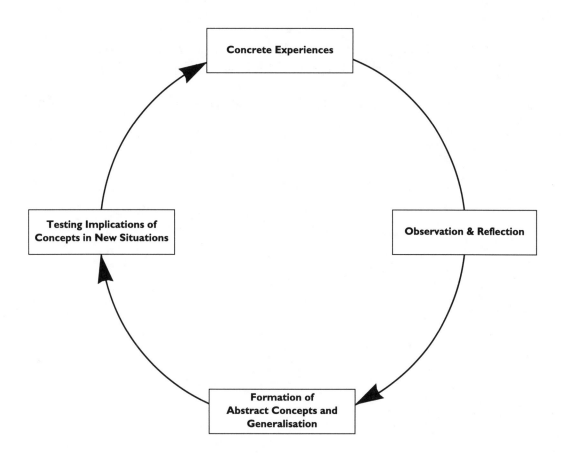

i) Provide an exercise for the students to participate in.

ii) Encourage them to reflect on it and sometimes observe it.

iii) Develop thoughts and ideas in discussion.

iv) Consider implications for familiar situations and where appropriate, experiment with new behaviours in practice.

This process will enable students to assess their learning.

Third, listen to and record what students are saying. This will provide you with considerable valuable evidence on the extent to which the aims and objectives were appropriate for the group; the extent to which they were met by the exercises that students took part in; and what additional benefit students obtained.

In the next section on Methodologies there are some strategies that will help you to elicit the information you need from students.

●●● *Methodologies*

The exercises in this handbook use participatory
groupwork. If this way of working is unfamiliar,
you may find it helpful to read through these notes
which describe the main methods. I also recommend
you to obtain a copy of Stanford's *Developing
Effective Classroom Groups.*

Typical participatory learning style!

WARM-UPS/ENERGISERS

If you are planning to work in a participative way with groups of students then
it will be important to build a repertoire
of warm-up games and energisers. These
are most commonly used at the start of a session, but they can also be used
when energy is flagging during a session or to make a break between two pieces
of work, especially if you want to change the pace. Sometimes it will be
appropriate to use them at the end of a session too, though you need to consider
in what mood the group will leave the room and what they are moving on to.
Rounds can also be used in this way (see below). There are examples of warm-
ups on page 78, and information on books which include classroom games can
be found in the resources section at the end.

ROUNDS

Rounds are a useful way of involving everyone, and developing group cohesion
and trust. They are most commonly used at the start or finish of a session,
where the group sits in a circle and each person in turn makes a contribution on
a theme (eg the best thing that has ever happened to me was...., my favourite
food is...., what I have learnt today is....). In the early days of a group it will be
important for you to 'model' it by going first, but as a group gains confidence
others may be willing to start it. This technique can also be useful at other times
in a session, especially if you sense that some people are finding it hard to
speak, because others are dominating the discussion or because a sensitive
subject is being discussed. It can be an effective and powerful form of
evaluation of a session or programme. Examples of the use of rounds are on
page 78.

QUIZZES

Quizzes are a useful way of handling the knowledge aspects of HIV and AIDS without using didactic methods. They can be used to re-inforce correct information that young people already have, to clarify areas where they are uncertain, provide new information and introduce discussion of sensitive issues in a safe format. Quizzes also provide an opportunity for large classes of students to become involved individually, in small groups and in whole group discussion. Two examples are given on pages 57-69.

BRAINSTORMING

Brainstorming is a method of generating a lot of ideas quickly. If the class is large it can be broken down into groups of about five or six; in a small class of less than about fifteen students, it may be possible to work in one group. Each group is given a large sheet of paper and a felt tip pen. Their task is to write down as many ideas as they can on a particular theme (eg all the things people might enjoy doing for relaxation, or all the words they know for heterosexuality – see page 127). It is important to make clear that exactly what is said must be written down, and no challenge or discussion is allowed. It can sometimes be useful to give a slightly different task to each group in order to compare responses.

CONTINUUMS

Continuums (or Four Corners of a Room) are now used in a wide variety of ways to explore values, attitudes and behaviours in a group setting. The idea is to represent the range of opinion in a group by asking people to take up a position on the continuum on a particular issue. The most common form is for the teacher to create a continuum on the floor using labels such as 'strongly agree' through to 'strongly disagree'. S/he reads out a statement (for examples see page 24) and individuals move to the position on the continuum which most nearly represents their view. When everybody has decided, they pair first with the person nearest them on the continuum, and sit down together. Each participant has one minute to explain to the other why they chose to stand in that position. They then return to the continuum and take a partner who stood in a different position and repeat the exercise. It is important that the pairing does not develop into a discussion – it is about listening and understanding. The exercise will work for any group of about twelve upwards, but the larger the group the more you will need firm control of the structure and timing. Some teachers find it useful to give out a sheet of statements beforehand for students to mark their position on a continuum.

CREATIVE THINKING

Several of the exercises need students to be creative. All of us have this ability to develop ideas from a knowledge base, but for many it lies untapped or has been stifled. If teachers encourage it, I believe students will develop the ability to use creative thinking effectively in many areas of their lives. Brainstorming (see above) is a relatively unthreatening way to introduce creative thinking; scenarios and role play (see below) are useful ways of developing it as a group gains confidence; and '100 Ways with a Condom' on page 97 and the guided fantasy in 'What Do I Want?' on page 95 rely on students' ability and willingness to think creatively. The latter exercise particularly will need sufficient safety in the group for students to 'let go'.

SCENARIOS

Scenarios provide a useful way of addressing situations and issues that students may not yet have experienced. By giving the group a scenario to work on, the issues become more real than can be created through general discussion. Students will often feel more comfortable with this than being asked to role play, because they can identify with a character without having to act it out. An example of the use of scenarios is on page 114. When you write a scenario it is important to make it realistic without being real – ie avoid names of people known to the students, or situations that they have been closely involved in.

ROLE PLAY

Role play is a widely used tool to explore feelings, attitudes and behaviours in a range of situations. Students may play themselves in unknown situations, such as telling a friend they are HIV positive; or an unknown person in a familiar situation, such as being their mother responding to her daughter coming home late. Role play can be acted out in front of the group, but many students find this quite daunting until they know and trust one another well. You may find it more successful to get them to work in small groups and report back to the whole class. Observers can be very useful. See page 103 for examples of use of role play. It is essential that time is given to de-roling. This is the process at the end of a role play exercise where you ensure that all students have put the role aside and returned to being themselves. There are some simple techniques for doing this – get everyone to change seats; ask them to share in pairs or with the group who they are in real life, what they had for breakfast, where they are going on holiday or what they did yesterday evening. One of these will be sufficient to bring most students back to real life, but occasionally a role play will have been particularly powerful for a group or an individual. You will probably notice that they are having difficulty answering the questions. In this situation you will need to work for several minutes to ensure that all those affected are free of the role.

DISCUSSION

Discussion with the whole class has long been a recognised learning method. It is essential to introduce a clear structure if students are to gain maximum value from it. Many students – and many adults – find it difficult to speak up in a large group especially if the topic is broadly defined. It may be helpful to set up a specific task in small groups of four to six students and ask each group to keep a record of the main points of the discussion. When they have completed the task in their small groups, bring them back together, and ask each group to make a brief presentation, lasting no more than two or three minutes. It may be appropriate to invite other groups to ask questions or comment on what has been said. If you then focus their attention on the key issues from the presentations, it is more likely that students will feel able to participate in discussion. Another way to generate discussion of a difficult or sensitive issue is to invite students to work first in self-selected small groups of two or three where they can feel safe enough to air their views. Then ask them to take their combined views into larger groups or into the whole group. Again, it will be important to ensure that each group gets a hearing before opening up general discussion. Examples of handling large groups for discussion appear on pages 55-56 and 70-71.

REFLECTION/REVIEW

The handbook uses several exercises which involve an element of reflection. This technique values the experience that students bring into the classroom and allows insights to be gained from the opportunity to reflect on that experience. It is also useful because it enables students to learn without necessarily having to share personal or sensitive material. The exercise on page 38 uses reflection in this way. Sometimes reflection is used following an exercise as part of the important process of reviewing and evaluating (see section on evaluation on page 8). It provides the opportunity for the group to think about what they have learnt, what else they would like to explore and how they might apply their learning to their own lives. It also provides useful feedback for the teacher. Reviews can be carried out individually, in small groups or as a whole class (see the section on Rounds above).

CONTRACTS/ACTION PLANS

A contract can be useful in helping students make changes in their lives, especially when in the course of a piece of work they discover something they are not happy with. If used carefully, monitored, supported and followed up, it can be a very powerful motivator for behaviour change. Where issues come up for a whole group a joint action plan, addressed in the same way, may be useful. A contract is devised by a student giving individual responses to a series of questions – What do I want to change? How will I do it? What barriers and difficulties might I encounter? How will I overcome them? What support will I need? By when do I expect to have achieved it? How will I celebrate?

It is important that the contract is written down and shared with another person or with the group, who can support and encourage if the going gets tough. Contracts in personal, social and health education mirror legal contracts in that they are a written statement of intent, binding and agreed between two or more people. An example of the use of contracts appears on pages 23 and 84, and action plans on page 23.

ATTENTION-OUT ACTIVITIES

'Attention-out' is an expression borrowed from counselling. At the end of an emotional or difficult session, the counsellor may need to help the client return to a state of mind where s/he can safely leave the session. A similar, though probably less intense situation may arise in a classroom when a group is dealing with issues around HIV and AIDS. You will sense that students have been 'pulled down' by an exercise and are left with unresolved negative feelings and thoughts. It is not appropriate to send them out of the classroom – whether to another lesson or to break or home in that state. Often this will be predictable, and you can plan for it by building in plenty of time for review, as in the exercise on page 127. However, sometimes it can be unexpected and you need to respond quickly. Explain what you are going to do and why, then use one or more of these techniques – tell students, in quick succession, to touch – for example – something red; something cold; something new; two things, one small and one large; somebody else and give them a hug. Or tell them to touch – hands with another person; noses with another person; then bottoms; feet with backs; ears with knees etc. In either case, continue for a few minutes until you feel the energy level has risen. Another less energetic way of changing attention is to a get students into pairs to share something positive, or do a round, such as 'what I am planning for this weekend is…' or 'my favourite way of spending a day is…'.

••• *Law and Guidance on AIDS Education*

It will be important for any teacher involved in planning AIDS education to become familiar with relevant legislation and guidance on sex education. The most significant extracts are reproduced here, and there are references for further reading on pages 152-153. The legislation applies to the whole of the United Kingdom, but the guidance quoted here only refers to England and Wales. Teachers in Scotland and Northern Ireland will need to obtain the relevant documents for their countries.

THE EDUCATION ACT (NO 2) 1986

The Education Act 1986 gives school governors the power to decide whether sex education shall be provided in school. It states that:

• Every school must have, and keep up to date, a written statement of its policy on sex education which is available to parents.

• Governors must have regard to any representations made by persons connected with the community served by the school.

• Sex education must be given in such a manner as to encourage pupils to have due regard to moral considerations and the value of family life.

THE EDUCATION ACT 1988

The Education Act 1988 introduced the National Curriculum, which lays down the foundation and core subjects which schools must teach. The requirements of the National Curriculum override any policy of the governing body. In addition, there is guidance on various aspects of the curriculum, including sex education within the cross-curricular theme of health education – this is non-statutory. In practice, this means that the sex education – and more recently the AIDS education – which appears in National Curriculum Science must be taught and that children may not be excluded from it. However, any additional sex education that a school wishes to provide, is at the discretion of the governing body.

DES (NOW DFE) CIRCULAR 11/87

Circular 11/87 provides guidance on sex education. It is mostly concerned with the compulsory period of schooling from age 5 to 16, but it says that many of the considerations will have implications for pupils above that age range. Reference is also made to pupils with special educational needs. It states that:

• Appropriate and responsible sex education is an important element in the work of schools in preparing pupils for adult life. It calls for sensitive treatment.

• Governors have discretion to accept or reject requests from parents for their children to be withdrawn from sex education provision. However, some parents will have strong objections on religious grounds to their children receiving sex education and governing bodies should fully appreciate this in exercising their discretion.

• Whilst the physical aspects of sexual behaviour may well be encompassed within the teaching of science opportunities for considering the broader emotional and ethical dimensions of sexual attitudes and mores may arise in other subject areas.

• The Secretary of State considers that the aims of a programme of sex education should be to present facts in an objective and balanced manner so as to enable pupils to comprehend the range of sexual attitudes and behaviour in present day society; to know what is and is not legal; to consider their own attitudes, and to make informed, reasoned and responsible decisions about the attitudes they will adopt while they are at school and in adulthood.

• Schools cannot, in general, avoid tackling controversial sexual matters by reason of their sensitivity. Pupils may well ask questions about them and schools should be prepared to offer balanced and factual information and to acknowledge the major ethical issues involved.

• There is no place in any school in any circumstances for teaching which advocates homosexual behaviour, which presents it as the 'norm', or which encourages homosexual experimentation by pupils. (See pages 106-107 for further discussion of homosexuality.)

• The government has emphasised that the key to limiting the spread of AIDS lies in enhanced public understanding about the disease and the ways in which infection is and is not transmitted. Schools can contribute towards the general level of awareness through the teaching which they offer. The Secretary of State believes that education about AIDS is an important element in the teaching programmes offered to pupils in the later years of compulsory schooling.

NATIONAL CURRICULUM GUIDANCE DOCUMENT 5

National Curriculum Guidance Document 5 states that:

• *Sex education provides an understanding that positive, caring environments are essential for the development of a good self image and that individuals are in charge of and responsible for their own bodies.*

• *Sex education provides knowledge about the processes of reproduction and the nature of sexuality and relationships, and encourages the acquisition of skills and attitudes which allow pupils to manage their relationships in a responsible and healthy manner.*

It is clear from the guidance which has come from the DFE and the NCC that schools are being encouraged to provide both sex education and AIDS education.

NATIONAL CURRICULUM SCIENCE KEY STAGE THREE

The National Curriculum Science Key Stage Three Programme of Study for Attainment Target 2 : Life and Living Processes states that:

• Pupils should extend their study of the ways in which the healthy functioning of the human body may be affected by diet, lifestyle, bacteria and viruses (including Human Immunodeficiency Virus), the abuse of solvents, tobacco, alcohol and other drugs, and how the body's natural defences may be enhanced by immunisation and medicines. They should study the human life cycle, including the physical and emotional changes that take place during adolescence, the physical and emotional factors necessary for the well-being of human beings in the early stages of their development, and understand the need to have a responsible attitude to sexual behaviour.

...1

'It's Nothing To Do With Me'

THINKING ABOUT THE ISSUES

INTRODUCTION

CLASSROOM ACTIVITIES

- Word Association
- Four Corners
- How Would It Be...?
- Risk Takers
- What If?

●●● *Introduction*

Young people (and many adults too) live by the motto 'It won't happen to me'. At this stage in their lives they are naturally risk takers and experimenters; they believe themselves to be immortal. These are very positive characteristics – they are what give young people their enthusiasm, commitment, energy, vitality, innocence and optimism.

It is not enough to teach the facts about HIV and AIDS, in the hope that this will frighten young people into behaving responsibly. We know that most young people have good information about HIV and AIDS, that they know what they ought to do to protect themselves. Yet all the evidence – both research and anecdotal – suggests that behaviour has barely changed at all. In between knowledge and the skills to put knowledge into practice, lies a huge area of feelings, beliefs, values and attitudes. It is these that need considerable attention before young people will recognise that 'it' could happen to them.

What Some Young People Say

'I don't think I'm that much at risk. I'm always very careful about who I sleep with.'

'AIDS will only get into you if you use dirty needles or if you are gay.'

'Blokes prefer their girlfriends to go on the pill, so they're having safe sex without a condom.'

'I'd always use a condom unless I knew the person – knew they hadn't got AIDS.'

'I wouldn't wear a condom if I knew in a guaranteed way that the person I was sleeping with didn't have any diseases of any kind.'

'We just stopped using a condom after we'd been going out for about four months.'

This section addresses feelings, beliefs, values and attitudes as they relate to HIV and AIDS generally, and may provide ideas for introductory work. Section 4 develops this theme at a more personal level.

You'd think with all this AIDS business, Ethel, patterns would carry a needle sharing warning!

●●● *Word Association*

This is a useful exercise to find out how pupils are feeling about HIV and AIDS and where work on emotions might appropriately start. It can be a powerful and thought-provoking exercise and needs plenty of time and follow up.

PURPOSE To identify feelings about HIV and AIDS, and to allow an opportunity to explore some of them.

AGE GROUP 11 – 18

LEVEL Requires some trust to have been built up in the group.
Does not require any pre-knowledge or understanding.

TIME NEEDED Minimum of 45 minutes, though it will depend how big the group is. This exercise should not be rushed, and it would be inadvisable to split it between sessions.

MATERIALS Small slips of paper.

METHOD 1. Give out several slips of paper to each person in the group. Tell them that you are going to say a word to them, and they should write down any words or very short phrases that come into their minds. They should write each word or phrase on a separate piece of paper, clearly so that others can read it. Tell the group that what they write down will be anonymous. Say the word 'AIDS' and repeat it every half minute or so. Allow about five minutes for this and discourage discussion.

2. When everybody is ready, ask them to pool the pieces of paper in the centre of the room, then re-distribute the papers roughly equally between everybody again.

3. Go round the group, asking each person to read out slowly what is on their piece of paper. When everyone has done this, ask them to lay the papers out on the floor for all to see.

4. Allow time now for everyone to walk around and read the papers. Their task is to choose one which has significance for them – personally relevant, a new thought or idea, something particularly difficult to contemplate or whatever. When they have chosen, they should pick up that piece of paper.

5. Ask students to choose a partner, or suggest that they work in small groups. Take three to five minutes per person to share their feelings and thoughts around the subject on their selected piece of paper. Explain that afterwards the whole group will come back together, and each person will be asked to make one simple

statement about the issue on their piece of paper.

6. Bring the group back together, and ask each person to contribute one statement about what is on their paper. You may well find that much of what is shared is quite heavy and negative, so it is important to be prepared to move a group on from this position. You might think some 'attention-out' activities would be useful at this point, (see page 15).

(see page 15)

REVIEW   Ask the group –

    To share any learning from the exercise

    For issues they would like to explore some more.

This will provide an agenda for further work. If they have been 'pulled down' by the exercise, you might also ask what they can do as individuals or as a group to change some of the negative or helpless 'messages' about AIDS. Make a list of actions, and encourage a contract (see page 15).

●●● *Four Corners*

Here is just one way of using a values continuum (see page 12). There are many other ways to use it, and you might like to experiment. Some teachers like to give out a sheet of statements at the start of the lesson and ask students individually to mark on a continuum their responses. This helps to overcome peer pressure during the active part of the exercise.

PURPOSE   To express attitudes towards issues raised by HIV and AIDS; to listen to the attitudes of others; and to evaluate our own thinking in the light of what we hear from others.

AGE GROUP   14 – 18

LEVEL   Requires some trust to have been built up in the group.
Does not require any pre-knowledge or understanding.

TIME NEEDED   Minimum of 45 minutes, though it will depend how many statements you use.

MATERIALS   Prepared cards for labelling the four corners.
Prepared statements (see page 26 for suggestions).
A timer or a watch.

METHOD   1. Ensure that you have a fairly large clear space, and have the group standing up in the space or sitting on chairs round the edge.

2. Label the four corners of the room in order – strongly agree, agree with reservations, disagree with reservations, strongly disagree.

3. Read out a controversial statement, and invite students to move to the corner which most nearly represents their stance. You may wish to allow them to stand between two positions or to be able to pass by standing in the middle of the room.

4. When everybody has had time to move, ask people to pair up with the person in the nearest position to them (or as near as possible). Include anyone who has chosen to pass or to stand between positions. When they have found a partner, ask them to sit down facing each other in their pair, and to take one minute each to tell their partner why they chose to stand where they did. You will need to keep time and emphasise that it is a listening exercise – it is not intended to develop into a discussion.

5. Bring them back to their original positions and ask them to pair up this time with someone in a different position from themselves. This can be quite tricky – the most confident people, who are often at the extremes, quickly identify a partner at the opposite extreme, leaving the less certain in the middle with much the same choice of partners as the first time round. It will help if you draw their attention to the instruction that they should find someone with a different rather than an opposite opinion. It can also be useful, (and fun), to suggest they should make eye contact with a partner, and only move to sit down when they are sure they have eye contact.

6. Again, they take a minute each to tell their new partner why they chose to stand where they did. Remind them that it is a listening exercise.

7. One statement could expand to fill a whole lesson. Or you may choose to move on and explore others in the same way. Probably, three or four statements will be plenty, and it is important to remember that the review is as important as the activity itself.

REVIEW   You may choose to do this after one or two statements or at the end of the session. Ask the group –
   How did you feel about taking a clear stance on this issue?
   Did peer pressure operate at all?
   How did it feel to be in a different position from the majority?
   Were you able to stick to the rule of not discussing?
   How did it feel not to be able to challenge or disagree?
   How did it feel to be listened to?
   Did anything surprise you?
This last question may elicit the comment that people in the same position are often there for different reasons or that people are in different positions for very similar reasons. This is a useful way in to exploring what happens normally in conversation –
   The extent to which we stereotype people and their views.
   The extent to which we really listen to people.
   The extent to which we surround ourselves with those we believe to hold similar views.
   The extent to which we want to convince others of our case rather than listening and attempting to understand theirs.

● ● ●

●●● SUGGESTED STATEMENTS FOR FOUR CORNERS

NB It is important that they are statements of opinion not fact. The best statements are likely to be those where there are a wide range of opinions, often because of different interpretations of the statement.

Safer sex means using a condom every time a person has sex

If you are married you won't get HIV infection

Drug users are irresponsible

It is best these days to have a sexual relationship only in marriage

People with AIDS deserve to be treated with respect and dignity

We hear too much about AIDS

Sex should be natural and spontaneous

Men/boys always want sex

Women are better at expressing feelings than men

All sex should lead to penetration

Condoms should be freely available

••• *How Would It Be...?*

An exercise similar to this was developed some years ago for use with year 10 students in a comprehensive school.

PURPOSE To consider the emotional, social and financial impact of HIV or AIDS on those who are infected, on their family and friends and on the community.

AGE GROUP 14 – 18

LEVEL Does not require high level of trust in group.
Does not require any pre-knowledge or understanding.

TIME NEEDED Minimum of 60 minutes. It would be possible to complete the exercise over two sessions, not too far apart, by breaking after Stage 3.

MATERIALS Copies of the case histories (see pages 28-33).
Copies of the table (see pages 34-35).

METHOD 1. Divide the students into six small groups of four to seven people each. Ask each group to select one student to act as chairperson.

2. Explain the purpose of the exercise. Give out copies of a different case history to each group (see pages 28-33) and one copy of the table (see pages 34-35). Ask the chairperson to read out the case history to the group, and to lead a discussion around the issues raised in the table, filling in the table as the discussion progresses. Allow about 20 minutes or so for this.

3. Meanwhile move around the groups, encouraging discussion and responding to factual questions.

4. When the tables are largely filled in, and the groups are ready, ask them to take a further ten minutes to identify the five most important issues that their case history has raised for them as a group. Have them write these on the large strips of paper, and arrange a visual display of their case history and the ensuing discussion.

5. Bring the whole group together again, and ask each small group in turn to report on their case. Have a general discussion on each one before moving to the next.

REVIEW End with a round of 'What I have learnt about the impact of HIV and AIDS on people is...'

•••

● ● ● CASE HISTORY I

NAME: WENDY   AGE: 28

For as long as she could remember, Wendy had wanted to be successful at three things – a hairdresser, a wife, and ultimately, a mother.

The first of these ambitions had been fulfilled. She was the chief cutter and stylist at a busy salon in her local town. The second ambition had also been fulfilled – she had been married for three years. Her husband, Brian, worked as a European representative for a large multi-national company, a job which required him to be away from home sometimes for as much as three or four weeks at a time. He had held this post for five years and quite understood that it was important for Wendy to have her own circle of friends to go out with while he was away.

Six months ago, while Brian was in Germany, she was invited to apply for the post of manager of one of a chain of hairdressing salons. She attended the interview, was offered the job and had a routine medical examination. She asked to be allowed to delay her acceptance until Brian returned and they could discuss the new job – because they had both been thinking that this was the ideal time to start a family.

Before she could talk to Brian about it, she was asked to go and see the doctor who had carried out the medical. She was told that she was HIV positive, and therefore they were unlikely to be able to employ her.

● ● ● CASE HISTORY 2

NAME: MICHAEL   **AGE: 35**

Michael is a haemophiliac and is HIV positive. He has been married for twelve years and has sons aged 10 and 3, and an 8 year old daughter.

He moved south from Barnsley in Yorkshire, his home town, about five years ago to take up a good teaching post in a rural comprehensive school. His mortgage is large and he and his wife find it hard to manage on his salary.

In the last year he has had several bouts of illness – he has lost a great deal of weight and is always tired. He realises that he cannot carry on as he is much longer.

● ● ●

● ● ● CASE HISTORY 3

NAME: JAMES   **AGE: 15**

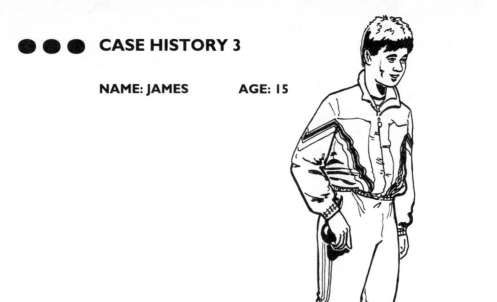

James lives in a large detached house in London. His father is a successful solicitor and his mother is a doctor. He has an older brother who is at Oxford. James is taking GCSEs this summer and would like to follow in his mother's footsteps as a doctor. He is a keen sportsman and plays in the school rugby team.

Ten years ago he had a serious road accident and was given a blood transfusion. His parents have often worried since that he might have become infected with HIV, but they talked it over with colleagues and decided not to have him tested.

However, recently they were contacted by the hospital where he was treated to say that there was some risk, and they advised testing. He has now been diagnosed HIV positive, though he is entirely well.

NAME: KATE   **AGE: 4**

Mike and Helen had been wanting a family of their own for years. After many tests it had been determined that a normal pregnancy for Helen was very unlikely, so they decided to adopt. They soon learnt that it would not be easy, and when they were offered Kate they were told that she might be HIV positive. This was confirmed when she was just over a year old. As soon as they saw her, they decided that she could not be rejected, and now she is their much loved daughter.

Mike is involved in developing computer software systems for a London-based company and he has to travel abroad quite often, but when he is at home he spends as much time as he can with her. They often go swimming, and he takes her to ballet and music classes.

It will be Kate's fifth birthday soon and she has invited twelve friends, some from school, some from ballet class and some from the neighbourhood, to come to her 'Teddy Bear's Picnic' party at the Happy Eater.

Until recently she has been pretty well, and her health is monitored by a London hospital. Her parents have avoided telling people why she makes periodic visits to London. However, in the last few weeks she has had several days off school and this week she was rushed into hospital with pneumonia.

● ● ●

●●● CASE HISTORY 5

NAME: JOE   **AGE: 45**

Joe is one of a family of five boys. He left school at fifteen, was persuaded against his will to become a plumber's apprentice, and eventually qualified. He disliked the routine, he disliked the roughness of his workmates and most of all he disliked the prospect of being a plumber for the rest of his working life.

He was never comfortable with women, so it was somewhat of a surprise to those who knew him when he married a girl he had known at school – and less of a surprise when the marriage didn't work out and they were divorced. At 27 he was on his own again. On impulse he quit his job, moved away from his home town and got a job as a travel courier, looking after holiday makers abroad.

He travelled a great deal, got to know a lot of people and, when off duty, frequented bars and clubs where he could mix with other men.

Last year, almost without warning, his health deteriorated. A visit to his doctor, then to the hospital for a series of tests, confirmed his condition. He had developed AIDS.

● ● ● CASE HISTORY 6

NAME: MARY   AGE: 22

Mary is personal secretary to the Sales Director of a big local company and shares a flat with two others. She is engaged to Sam, a research chemist in the same company, and they are hoping to buy a house. They will need two salaries when they apply for a mortgage. Sam's widowed mother doesn't think Mary is 'good enough' for her only son.

However, Mary and Sam are very happy and often visit Mary's family. They like to baby-sit for her two nieces, aged 4 and 6, who adore them.

Mary did her secretarial training at a local college where, through a previous boyfriend, she came into contact with a drug using crowd. She tried intravenous drugs once, but was frightened of what might happen to her and decided not to experiment again. Anyway, Sam came on the scene soon afterwards.

Recently, she went along to a blood donor session at the company she works for. She found out that she was HIV positive when they tested her blood before using it.

● ● ●

●●● | TABLE FOR THE CASE HISTORIES

NAME	
AGE	
OCCUPATION	
STATE OF HEALTH	
EMOTIONAL EFFECT ON PERSON	
SOCIAL EFFECT ON PERSON	
FINANCIAL EFFECT ON PERSON	

EMOTIONAL EFFECT ON FAMILY/FRIENDS	
SOCIAL EFFECT ON FAMILY/FRIENDS	
FINANCIAL EFFECT ON FAMILY/FRIENDS	
EFFECT ON OTHER PEOPLE	

●●● *Risk Takers*

This exercise makes a useful introduction to work on information around HIV and AIDS, by exploring the idea of risk-taking.

PURPOSE To explore our own and other people's risk-taking behaviour; and to consider the links between risk-taking and responses to HIV and AIDS.

AGE GROUP 14 – 18

LEVEL Requires some trust to have been built up in the group.
Does not require any pre-knowledge or understanding.

TIME NEEDED Minimum of 45 minutes.

METHOD 1. Have the questions ready on a flipchart or blackboard.

2. Explain the purpose of the exercise.

3. Ask students to work alone for 5 minutes or so, thinking about an occasion in their lives when they took a risk – it may be something quite trivial or something really significant. If you are well into a programme and there is a high level of trust in the group, it may be appropriate to suggest they consider a time when they took a sexual or drug-using risk. When they are ready have them write down their responses to the following questions –
What factors influenced your decision to take a risk?
What were you feeling at the time?
What was the outcome of taking that risk? Was it positive or negative?
Do you see yourself generally as a risk-taker?
How do you view risk-taking in others?

4. Invite students to choose two or three other people to work with. Take 3-5 minutes each to share what you choose of the risk-taking incident and your responses to it. Note particularly any differences in responses to risk-taking.

5. Bring the whole group back together and discuss –
Are there different kinds of risks?
To what extent do we weigh up risks?
In what circumstances do people take risks?
Do people modify behaviour in the light of outcomes?
Are others viewed more or less as risk-takers than ourselves?

REVIEW Go back into the same small groups. In the light of the plenary discussion, what does it tell you about people's responses to HIV infection and AIDS –

Why do some people appear to ignore or play down the risk?

Why do others seem to get very frightened?

What can we do to put the risk in perspective?

If you are using this as an introduction to information on HIV and AIDS, you might suggest that students bear in mind their personal responses to risk when discussing information.

●●● *What If?*

This is an activity that can be adapted to many different situations.

PURPOSE   To challenge the assumption that HIV infection always happens to 'other people out there'; to explore with students the impact that HIV infection would have on them and on their relationships; and to encourage thoughtfulness towards those who are infected.

AGE GROUP   14 – 18

LEVEL   Requires some trust to have been built up in the group.
Requires some pre-knowledge and understanding.

TIME NEEDED   Minimum of 45 minutes. It would be possible to complete the exercise over two sessions, not too far apart, by breaking after Stage 3.

METHOD   1. Give each student pen and paper. Ask them to divide their page in half lengthways.

2. Explain that on the left hand side they should write down about twelve things they expect to enjoy doing in the next ten years – this might be work or career plans; hobbies, interests or ways of spending leisure time; relationships; ambitions or dreams. Stress that this list is personal and they will not have to share it with anyone else.

3. When the lists are complete ask the group to divide the right hand side of the page into four vertical columns.

4. Then ask them to code their lists as instructed. Give one instruction at a time, and allow time for completion before moving on to the next.

5. Ask them to put a pound sign at the top of the first column and to mark anything on their list which would cost more than £100 in a year. At the top of the second column write the word 'health' and put a mark beside anything that would require health and fitness. At the top of the third column put the word 'people', and mark anything on the list that requires contact with others. At the top of the fourth column put the word 'AIDS', and ask them to mark anything it might be difficult to do if they had AIDS.

REVIEW When the coding is complete, ask students to review their lists individually, focusing on the following questions –

Are there any patterns in what you have marked?

What would you be able to do if you were HIV positive?

What would affect your ability to do what you wanted?

What would you be able to do if you had AIDS?

What would now affect your ability to do what you wanted?

Are there any surprises?

Have students complete sentence stems –

I was surprised to find that...

I feel...

I became aware that...

In small groups of three or four discuss the completed sentences.

As a whole group discuss –

Whether the exercise was useful

What did it bring up?

What did you learn from it?

● ● ●

2

'Not AIDS Again!'

UNDERSTANDING THE FACTS

INTRODUCTION

INFORMATION ABOUT HIV AND AIDS

STATISTICS ON HIV AND AIDS

CLASSROOM ACTIVITIES
- **· Graffiti Sheets**
- **· Risk Card Game**
- **· Quizzes**
- **· What is Safer Sex?**
- **· Safe or Not?**

●●● *Introduction*

Most teachers start by providing accurate and up-to-date information about HIV and AIDS, and it is the element of AIDS education which is compulsory as part of National Curriculum Science.

There is no doubt that most young people should know about viruses, the immune system and modes of transmission as part of their scientific education. There is now very strong research evidence though, to suggest that this knowledge makes little or no difference to sexual decision making. What is learnt in a traditional biology lesson is so divorced from 'real life' that young people do not make the connection between what they learn and their own behaviour. If we wish to use these lessons to provide information that can be used by young people in their lives outside school, then the approach needs to be modified.

We need to find out what they already know – which from research evidence is quite a lot – and build on this. Sometimes this will involve confirming and reinforcing correct information; sometimes it will involve modifying or putting right mis-information; and sometimes adding new information. If we start from what is already known, the pupils are more likely to be interested than if we assume too much or too little knowledge.

An excellent way of checking out what pupils know and where their uncertainties lie, is to use a quiz. This is not with the purpose of testing them, but rather as a discussion starter. Two examples of quizzes are included here. For those pupils who are less confident with written material there is a card game, which encourages active participation and illustrates risks clearly and visibly.

I believe that information about HIV and AIDS needs to include information on safer sex and on drug use. Young people do not find it easy to get information on which sexual behaviours are safe and which are not; nor on how to minimise the risks from drug use. Often their only source of information is their friends, and research evidence tells us how unreliable this is likely to be. Two exercises about safer sex are included here, (see pages 70-73).

In all these exercises it will be important that you are confident with the information at a personal as well as a scientific level. One of the difficulties that HIV has posed is that there are few answers – much of what we know has developed over the last ten years or so, is constantly developing and being modified. You will not be able to give categorical answers to your students; they, like you, have to learn to live with uncertainty. The information which follows here and in the answers to the quizzes attempts to provide accurate and up-to-date information, whilst recognising the 'grey' areas.

●●●

Tests reveal Aids virus is spreading in heterosexuals

Aids:
Diana hears of epidemics second wave

Evidence of an epidemic among heterosexuals has proved to be a myth

Pointless panic on Aids

THE THREATENED explosion of Aids cases among hetero-sexuals is not happening.

Epidemic feared as Aids affects 2,000 heterosexuals

Low Aids risk for sexually active women, study says

Aids virus 'could be spread by a passionate kiss'

AIDS COULD KILL TWO MILLION, DOCTOR SAYS

'Aids warnings for heterosexuals are misleading'

AIDS threat 'on increase for non-gays'

Aids: Women in the front line

●●●

●●● *Information About HIV and AIDS*

It is important to make a clear distinction between HIV and AIDS. The media has thoroughly confused most people by talking about 'catching AIDS', 'AIDS tests' and 'the AIDS virus'. They produce images of people with AIDS, nearly always sick and dying. If we fail to distinguish between HIV and AIDS there is a danger that young people will go on believing that they will be able to identify someone who is infected because they will look sick.

HIV (Human Immuno-deficiency Virus) is a virus, and AIDS (Acquired Immune Deficiency Syndrome) is a pattern of diseases which may result from that infection. So anyone could theoretically catch the virus, but nobody catches AIDS.

When a virus gets into the bloodstream, the body responds by producing antibodies to the infection. This forms part of the immune response. Often an infection can be counteracted by the production of antibodies. However HIV is a retro virus which sets out to destroy the immune system itself. At first the body may respond successfully, but gradually the ability of the body to fight off infection is reduced. This is why people who have been infected with HIV often develop one or more of a whole range of diseases collectively known as AIDS – their immune system is no longer able to resist infection by many other organisms.

The progression of HIV infection is significant (see diagram on page 45). There has to be exposure to the virus for infection to occur. This does not come from normal social contact with people. It is recognised that there are only three main ways in which infection is likely to happen : through unprotected sexual intercourse (anal or vaginal); through sharing equipment to inject drugs; or from contaminated blood or blood products, which includes transmission from an infected mother to her baby.

There has been a great deal of concern about transmission to babies. This may happen in two ways, at or around the time of birth or through breast milk. An HIV positive mother is likely to pass on her HIV antibodies to her child at or just before birth. This is part of the normal process by which a baby is given protection in the early months of life. Evidence from a recent European Study suggests that less than 30% of HIV positive mothers will also pass on the virus, and in Britain that figure appears to be more like 14%. A mother has to wait until her baby is up to eighteen months old to know whether it is infected or not. It seems likely that if a woman has a T helper cell count below 500 she is at increased risk of producing an infected child.

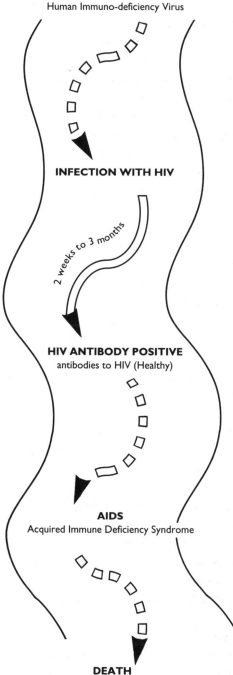

EXPOSURE TO HIV
Human Immuno-deficiency Virus

INFECTION WITH HIV

2 weeks to 3 months

HIV ANTIBODY POSITIVE
antibodies to HIV (Healthy)

AIDS
Acquired Immune Deficiency Syndrome

DEATH

KEY
Possible progression

Definite progression

The same study suggests that breastfeeding is riskier than we thought – there are now many cases of apparent infection through breast milk worldwide, and HIV positive mothers in this country are being advised not to breastfeed.

As with other viruses, exposure to HIV does not necessarily lead to infection. There will be a whole range of reasons for this. First, the quantity and quality of virus and the mode of transmission will be crucial. A model of transmission (see diagram on page 47) may be useful when considering the likelihood of HIV infection from a particular source. The chain must remain unbroken if infection is to occur. Second, the health state of the potential exposee will be significant. If we consider the factors that influence whether a person catches flu, we know that it is more likely when they are 'run down', tired, stressed or overworked. This is because any of these factors lower the ability of the immune system to fight off infection. We also know that the immune system is boosted by healthy food and plenty of exercise. Third, the presence of co-factors will increase the risk. These include genital ulceration, other STDs or a partner who has AIDS. The latter is because infectivity increases with progression to AIDS. Fourthly, a person can take precautions to protect themselves. Condoms, used properly, will considerably reduce the risk of transmission during vaginal or anal sex; avoiding shared needles and syringes, or flushing them through several times, first with bleach and then with water, will reduce the risk with intravenous drug use; and sensible hygiene precautions will protect from infection with spilled blood.

When a person is infected with the virus, the immune system responds by making antibodies. This takes a little while. The most commonly used test to establish whether a person has been infected with HIV looks for antibodies. It is called the HIV antibody test. It is normally carried out at least three months after likely infection because it may take as long as this for antibodies to show in the test. The time between infection taking place and antibodies showing up is called the window period.

Once a person has antibodies to HIV they are known as HIV antibody positive (or HIV+ for short). If they have had a test they will know this, but they could be infected without knowing it. They may have experienced some mild symptoms at the time of infection; the symptoms may be so slight that they do not notice them; or they may have had no symptoms. A person may then feel and look well for many years, but they will be able to infect others.

If the virus starts to damage the immune system, more serious and noticeable symptoms will appear. These result from the inability of the immune system to deal effectively with infection. They are very wide ranging and vary in intensity and pattern from person to person. The most common clinical predictors of progression are diarrhoea, weight loss, night sweats, fatigue, shingles or a variety of mouth and skins conditions.

● ● ● TRANSMISSION OF HIV

We can envisage transmission in terms of a 'chain' which must not be broken in any place if infection is to occur –

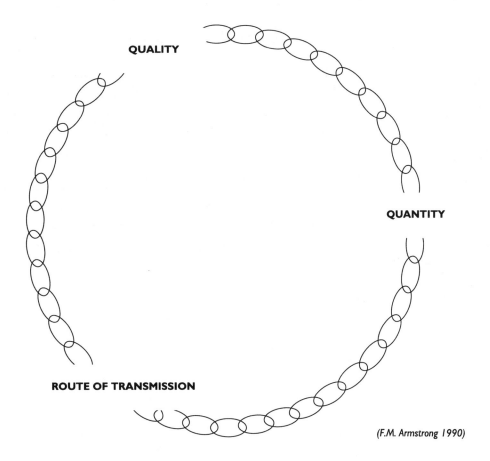

QUALITY

QUANTITY

ROUTE OF TRANSMISSION

(F.M. Armstrong 1990)

For the virus to be transmitted three things must be present;

• There must be an adequate quantity of virus present to cause infection – this is most likely to occur with blood semen, vaginal and cervical fluids (and possibly with breast milk) which contain the highest concentrations of virus.

• The virus must be of suitable quality to cause infection i.e. undamaged by heat, bleach, or chemicals (for example acid).

• There must be a suitable route for the virus to reach the particular cells for which it has an affinity.

Reproduced by kind permission of Ewan Armstrong

A person may also develop other rare conditions like Kaposi's sarcoma, a form of skin cancer, or Pneumocystis carinii, a form of pneumonia. Some people will have periods of illness, sometimes needing hospital treatment, and will have long periods in between when they are sufficiently well to work and lead a normal life. The health of others may deteriorate quite quickly.

Doctors use a blood test, in which they count the level of T helper cells, to decide how far HIV infection has progressed. When the T helper cell count drops below 200 (above 500 is normal) the person is at greatly increased risk of developing one of the life-threatening diseases which characterise AIDS. Treatments are available to alleviate symptoms, and antiretroviral drugs, such as AZT and DDI are being used successfully to slow the progression of infection, but there is as yet no cure.

Of the people who were diagnosed HIV positive more than ten years ago, some are still well, some now have AIDS and many have died. We do not yet know enough about why people respond very differently to HIV infection, and we cannot be sure that all people who are HIV positive will eventually go on to develop AIDS.

••• *Statistics on HIV and AIDS*

GLOBAL STATISTICS

Estimates taken in 1991 indicate that worldwide there are –

- 1 million adults with AIDS

- 1/2 million children with AIDS

- 8-10 million adults with HIV infection

- 1 million children with HIV infection

Vaginal intercourse accounts for 70% of HIV infection worldwide.

The developing world accounts for more than 80% of HIV infection.

By the year 2000 estimates indicate that worldwide there will be –

- 10 million adults with AIDS

- 30-40 million adults and children with HIV infection

- 10 million children orphaned

It is expected that South America and South East Asia will be especially affected.

Incidence of infection globally –

- blood transfusion makes up 3-5% of cases

- perinatal infection makes up 5-10% of cases

- sexual intercourse makes up 70-80% of cases

- IVDU makes up 5-10% of cases

- needle stick injuries to healthcare workers make up 0.01% of cases

UK STATISTICS

23,276 people in the UK are known to have HIV infection or AIDS

- 5648 with AIDS

- 5295 are male

- 353 are female

- 3527 have died

- the remainder have HIV infection

11% of the people with HIV infection or AIDS are women

- 87% of infected women are between 15 and 34 years old

- 52% of women with AIDS were infected through heterosexual sex

- of these, 20% were infected by intercourse with a 'high risk' partner

- 67% by intercourse with a non-high risk partner from abroad

- 13% by intercourse with a non-high risk partner from the UK

Up to 1985, 2% of HIV infection was as a result of heterosexual sex; by 1991 this was 24%.

Infection rates from anonymous testing show that 1 in 500 pregnant women in metropolitan London is HIV infected. This is a fourfold increase in three years.

Sources of Further Statistical Information

Clift and Stears' *AIDS : The Secondary Scene.*

Statistical updates should be available through local health education/ promotion units.

●●● *Graffiti Sheets*

This can be a useful introduction to a programme on HIV and AIDS. It raises many issues and will indicate to you what kind of knowledge and beliefs your students have.

PURPOSE

To encourage students to start talking about HIV and AIDS; and to help the teacher assess the needs of the group.

AGE GROUP

11 – 18

LEVEL

Does not require high level of trust in group.
Does not require any pre-knowledge or understanding.

TIME NEEDED

About 45 minutes. It would be possible to complete the exercise over two sessions, not too far apart, by breaking after Stage 2 or 3.

METHOD

1. Pin up several large sheets of paper around the room, headed 'AIDS'. Have a box of felt tip pens for the group to use.

2. Invite everybody to mill about and write any statements they like about AIDS on the sheets – things they know about AIDS; things they have heard; things people say.

3. When each sheet has at least five or six 'graffiti' written on it, divide the class into small groups of three to five students and give each group one of the graffiti sheets. Their task is to discuss the statements and sort them into –
    Things that they believe to be true.
    Things that they believe are untrue.
    Things they are uncertain or disagree about.
Ask them to use a symbol, such as a tick, a cross or a question mark, to indicate their decision on each statement. Allow about ten to fifteen minutes for this, depending on the number of statements and the size of group.

4. Bring the class back together again, and have each group report back. Invite other groups to challenge or offer new information. Change symbols as necessary. At this stage do not be tempted to give information or correct misinformation. This exercise leads very effectively into a quiz. Most of the issues that are likely to have been raised will probably be covered by the quizzes offered on pages 57-69. However, you may want to adapt them or write your own, based on what the students have identified. If you are moving straight on to a quiz, pin the sheets back up on the wall. If you are planning to do the quiz next lesson, save the sheets, and pin them up at the start of the next lesson.

REVIEW   After the quiz it will be valuable to go back to the graffiti sheets. Encourage the class (in small groups first perhaps) to identify any misinformation they had, and to check whether uncertainties have been clarified. Discuss their learning from the exercise –

What have they learnt?

Were there any surprises?

How do they feel about the information now?

Will it make any difference to them?

●●● *Risk Card Game*

A very useful exercise to use in conjunction with the quiz, to reinforce information visually; or for use with a group who have difficulties with written material.

PURPOSE   To reinforce messages about what activities are and are not risky; and to explore personal responses to risk.

AGE GROUP   11 – 18

LEVEL   Does not require high level of trust in group.
Does not require any pre-knowledge or understanding.

TIME NEEDED   Minimum of 45 minutes, though it will depend how big the group is, how many cards you use and how much discussion is generated.

MATERIALS   A set of cards (see below).
Copies of 'Transmission of HIV' diagram (see page 47).
A copy of 'Answers to the Quiz' (see pages 58-60).

METHOD   1. Prepare a set of cards (roughly A5 size), each with an activity written or drawn on it that is popularly believed to carry some risk of HIV infection. Have at least one card per person in the group. Also prepare three cards entitled: high risk, some risk and no risk. Some teachers like to use a 'don't know' card as well – it enables students to express genuine uncertainty or to raise questions about the risks which are deliberately stated ambiguously. However, it also allows students to 'cop out' from making judgements.

2. Have the group sitting in a circle. Explain the purpose of the activity, and that the group is going to create a continuum of risk down the middle of the floor.

3. Place the 'high risk' card at one end of the continuum; the 'some risk' card about three quarters of the way along; and the 'no risk' card at the other end.

SUGGESTED ACTIVITIES

- hugging

- kissing

- sharing cups

- sitting on toilet seats

- being spat on

- using someone else's razor

- having a friend pierce your ears

- sharing needles for IV drug use

- using drugs

- giving blood

- having a blood transfusion

(continued overleaf)

---

4. Ask each person in turn to read out what is on their card, place it where they think it belongs on the continuum and make a statement about why they have placed it there. At this point, invite others to challenge if they disagree about where it has been placed. Encourage sharing of information and responses to that knowledge. It may be useful to introduce the Transmission Diagram at this point; to discuss 'what if' scenarios; and to consider with the group the likelihood of this scenario occurring. Provide additional information as appropriate and attempt to agree a position on the continuum for each activity. Continue this process until all the cards have been placed.

5. Look at the continuum with the group and draw out the visual messages.

SUGGESTED ACTIVITIES

- cleaning up spilled blood

- giving mouth-to-mouth resuscitation

- being operated on by an HIV positive surgeon

- being bitten by mosquitoes

- having unprotected vaginal sex

- having unprotected anal sex

- having unprotected oral sex

- masturbating

- HIV+ mother infecting her baby

- eating food prepared by someone who is HIV positive

- working alongside someone with AIDS

REVIEW Divide the students into small groups of three or four to discuss and report back on –

What did we learn about transmission of HIV?
Are there still risks we are uncertain about?
How do we feel about the information now?
Did anything surprise us?
Will it make any difference to us?

● ● ●

●●● *Quizzes*

These are a good way of checking out what students know, and of raising difficult or embarrassing subjects in a fairly safe way.

PURPOSE
For students to confirm what they know; to identify areas of uncertainty or lack of knowledge; and to provide an opportunity for students to discuss and gain new information.

AGE GROUP
11 – 18 (according to the quiz you use)

LEVEL
Does not require high level of trust in group.
Does not require any pre-knowledge or understanding.

TIME NEEDED
Minimum of 45 minutes, though it will depend how long the quiz is, how much prior knowledge the group has and how much discussion is generated. It would be possible to complete the exercise over two sessions by breaking after Stage 4 or during stage 5.

MATERIALS
Copies of a quiz.
Copies of 'Transmission of HIV' and 'Progression of HIV Infection' diagrams (see pages 45 and 47).
A copy of 'Answers to the Quiz' (see pages 58-60 and pages 64-69).

METHOD
1. Prepare an appropriate quiz for students. Use the examples given here as a guide (see pages 57 and 64-69), but remember to write it with your students in mind – you will need to consider their age and gender; level of maturity and ability; previous knowledge and experience; and what issues you want to raise.

2. Explain the purpose of the exercise, and emphasise that it is not a test, nobody else need see what they have written and it is as much about discussion as about right or wrong answers.

3. Give out the quizzes and ask students to fill them in individually first of all. This will probably take about 5-10 minutes.

4. When everybody has finished, encourage them to divide into small groups no bigger than fours and share answers, noting disagreements and questions. Allow about 15 minutes for this.

5. Bring the group back together to go through each question. Encourage discussion, further questions and challenge. This process can take from one to two hours, depending on the length of the quiz and the interest of the students.

REVIEW   Invite the students to return to the small groups they used earlier in the exercise and discuss –

What have they learnt?

Is there anything else they want to know about?

How do they feel about the information now?

Were there any surprises?

What difference will it make?

●●● **AIDS TRUE OR FALSE QUIZ**

Are the following statements true or false?

1. **Anyone can catch AIDS.**

2. **Women are as likely as men to get infected with HIV.**

3. **Only sexually active people are at risk of HIV infection.**

4. **There is no risk of HIV infection if I check my partner's sexual history.**

5. **If I avoid penetrative sex (vaginal, anal or oral) there is no risk of HIV infection.**

6. **Condoms provide considerable protection against HIV infection.**

7. **An HIV positive woman should avoid pregnancy.**

© LDA Yes, AIDS Again

● ● ● AIDS TRUE OR FALSE QUIZ

ANSWERS AND DISCUSSION POINTS

1. Anyone can catch AIDS.

ANSWER   **FALSE.**
Nobody catches AIDS. AIDS is a pattern of diseases which may result from infection with HIV.

DISCUSSION POINTS   The difference between HIV and AIDS, and the significance of making that distinction (see diagram on page 45).
Transmission, progression, prognosis, treatment, prevention.

2. Women are as likely as men to get infected with HIV.

ANSWER   **TRUE.**
Women are quite as susceptible to HIV infection as men. In fact the evidence from sexual transmission of HIV shows that women are roughly twice as likely to become infected as men.

DISCUSSION POINTS   Why has HIV been associated with gay men?
Evidence for heterosexual transmission.
Risk to lesbian women.

3. Only sexually active people are at risk of HIV infection.

ANSWER   **FALSE.**
Sexual activity is one form of possible transmission, but another is the sharing of needles and syringes for IV drug use.

DISCUSSION POINTS   Evidence for routes of transmission.
Confused messages about risks from 'drug use' as opposed to 'sharing needles and syringes'. Why might this be?
Is there any way in which drug use generally might create an HIV infection risk?

4. There is no risk of HIV infection if I check my partner's sexual history.

ANSWER   **FALSE.**

There is no way that asking a partner for their sexual history can ensure safety from HIV infection. The partner cannot know the history of all his or her partners; s/he may not remember all of them; s/he may choose not to tell the truth. However, talking about ourselves is a valuable part of the process of getting to know each other.

DISCUSSION POINTS   How easy is it to ask about a partner's sexual history?

How easy is it to tell the truth?

Is there any way that anyone can know whether their partner is putting them at risk? What is the place of trust in a relationship?

If we cannot know, then what can we do?

5. If I avoid penetrative sex (vaginal, anal or oral) there is no risk of HIV infection.

ANSWER   **FALSE.**

Avoiding unprotected penetrative sex could considerably reduce the risk of sexually transmitted HIV infection, however, it would depend what other sexual activities replaced it and whether the person was involved in any other risky activities such as IV drug use.

DISCUSSION POINTS   Are all forms of penetrative sex equally risky?

What alternatives are there to penetrative sex? How safe are they?

How important is penetrative sex for women and for men?

What do we mean by 'safer sex'?

6. Condoms provide considerable protection against HIV infection.

ANSWER   **TRUE.**

Condoms provide a very high level of protection, though they cannot guarantee safety. However, the likelihood of transmission of HIV coinciding with condom failure is several million to one against. The lower the initial risk (ie oral sex is less risky than vaginal sex, and vaginal sex is less risky than anal sex) the greater the protection that the condom can provide.

DISCUSSION POINTS   When the evidence for the use of condoms is so strong, why are they still not being widely used?

Feelings about women carrying condoms?

What are the alternatives to condom use?

7. **An HIV positive woman should avoid pregnancy.**

ANSWER   **FALSE.**

There is no 'should' about it. An HIV positive woman who has been given good information will be able to make her own decision about the risks of pregnancy. In Europe less than 15% of babies born to HIV positive mothers are themselves infected. There does seem to be a small risk of infection from breast milk, and in this country women who are HIV positive are being advised to bottle feed.

DISCUSSION POINTS   The confusion over the evidence of risk.

Is this a risk a woman should be allowed to take?

What might the difficulties be for an HIV+ mother?

● ● ●   WHAT DO I KNOW ABOUT AIDS? QUIZ

Tick the following if the answer is yes.

1. Can anyone catch AIDS?

2. HIV (the AIDS virus) has been SHOWN to be transmitted through which of the following body fluids:

blood?	breast milk?	saliva?
vomit?	semen?	faeces?
sweat?	urine?	vaginal fluids?
tears?		

3. What is the risk of catching HIV from:	HIGH RISK	SOME RISK	NO RISK
Hugging			
Kissing			
Sharing cups			
Sitting on toilet seats			
Being spat on			
Using someone else's razor			
Having a friend pierce your ears			
Sharing needles for IV drug use			
Using drugs			
Giving blood			

(continued overleaf)

	HIGH RISK	SOME RISK	NO RISK
Having a blood transfusion			
Cleaning up spilled blood			
Giving mouth-to-mouth resuscitation			
Being operated on by an HIV positive surgeon			
Being bitten by mosquitoes			
Having unprotected vaginal sex			
Having unprotected anal sex			
Having unprotected oral sex			
Masturbating			
An HIV positive mother			
Eating food prepared by someone who is HIV positive			
Working alongside someone with AIDS			

4. If a person is HIV antibody positive:

Have they got AIDS?

Will they be dead in five years?

Will they be infectious to other people?

Will you be able to tell?

Is their sex life over?

5. If you were worried about HIV or AIDS, and wanted information or a test, who would you talk to:

Your GP

An AIDS Helpline

A teacher

Your family

Your friends

The GUM Clinic (Special/STD Clinic) at your local hospital

ANSWERS AND DISCUSSION POINTS

1. **Can anyone catch AIDS?**

ANSWER **NO**

Nobody catches AIDS. AIDS is a pattern of diseases which may result from infection with HIV.

DISCUSSION POINTS The difference between HIV and AIDS, and the significance of making that distinction (see diagram on page 45).
Transmission, progression, prognosis, treatment, prevention.

2. **HIV (the AIDS virus) has been SHOWN to be transmitted through which of the following body fluids:**

blood?	breast milk?
saliva?	vomit?
semen?	faeces?
sweat?	urine?
vaginal fluids?	tears?

ANSWER **BLOOD, SEMEN, VAGINAL FLUIDS AND BREAST MILK**

The evidence for the first three is clear and widespread; the evidence for breast milk is as yet less clear. The key word is 'transmitted', since HIV has been found in other body fluids, but there is no evidence of transmission (see diagram on page 47).

DISCUSSION POINTS People seem to get more frightened by the risk from saliva than from semen or vaginal fluids. Why might this be?
The different advice being given to women in different parts of the world about breastfeeding.

3. **Can HIV be caught from:**

Hugging : **NO RISK**
There is no transmission of body fluids.

How easy would it be to hug someone you knew to have AIDS?

Kissing : **NO RISK**

In dry kissing there is no transmission of body fluids. In wet (French or deep) kissing, there may be transmission of saliva or even blood. There is no evidence that saliva can transmit HIV. Any blood is likely to be much diluted by saliva and the virus to be inactivated by the acid in the stomach.

Sharing cups : **NO RISK**

Again, there is no evidence of transmission through saliva.

Sitting on toilet seats : **NO RISK**

Any blood or semen on a toilet seat is likely to be dry. If it was very fresh, it would be visible and could only transmit HIV if the person sitting on the seat had a cut or sore which came into direct contact with it.

How likely is this?

Being spat on : **NO RISK**

Again, no evidence of transmission through saliva.

Using someone else's razor : **SOME RISK**

There would have to be a quantity of fresh blood on the razor, and the person using it would have to cut themselves. The virus would also have to find its way past outflowing blood. The risk might be greater in places where HIV infection is likely and shared razors are common, eg institutions. It is not a good idea for general hygiene reasons to share razors.

Having a friend pierce your ears : **SOME RISK**

The danger here is that it is often a group activity, and some blood may be left on the needle. Any activity that involves possible transmission through blood, including tattooing, should be discouraged unless carried out under strict hygiene regulations. The 'blood brothers' practice is particularly risky.

Sharing needles for IV drug use : **HIGH RISK**

Sharing needles, syringes or any other equipment for intravenous drug use is very dangerous because infected blood could be injected direct into the bloodstream. Harm minimisation programmes take the line that the best protection is not to use drugs at all; if you must use drugs, then don't inject them; if you must inject, then don't share needles or other equipment; and if you must share, then rinse out the syringe and needle three times in bleach and three times in water.

Using drugs : **SOME RISK**

It is important to distinguish between the sharing of needles and syringes and other drug using behaviour. However, if a person is under the influence of drugs, including alcohol, they may not make the best decisions for themselves. There is therefore an indirect risk from a wide range of recreational drug use.

Giving blood : **NO RISK**

In this country sterile needles are used, and there is no contact with other people's blood.

Having a blood transfusion : **SOME RISK**

In this country there is a voluntary system of blood donation, and donors are asked not to give blood if they are linked with any of the high risk groups. All donated blood is now tested. There is a minute risk that a newly infected donor could give blood during the 'window' period, before antibodies have developed. However, it is important to remember that blood transfusions are only given when a person is seriously ill, and the risk from refusing a transfusion is far greater than the risk of receiving infected blood.

DISCUSSION POINTS Is the situation similar in all countries?

What precautions can a traveller take?

Cleaning up spilled blood : **SOME RISK**

All blood should be treated with caution, and good hygiene precautions followed. Cuts or sores, especially on the hands, should be covered with a waterproof plaster; disposable gloves should be worn if they are available; and blood should be cleaned up using bleach and disposable cloths. If a person is bleeding profusely, use any material to hand, like a towel, T shirt or kitchen roll to create a barrier between the helper and the patient. If blood gets on the skin, wash it off with hot water and soap.

Giving mouth-to-mouth resuscitation : **NO RISK**

Since saliva does not transmit the virus, there is no risk. A small amount of blood can be wiped away. If there is bleeding from the mouth an amateur should not give mouth-to-mouth resuscitation. Professionally trained personnel use some kind of barrier between themselves and the patient. This is as much to do with good general hygiene practice as with HIV infection.

DISCUSSION POINTS Would you not give mouth-to-mouth resuscitation for fear of catching HIV infection?

Being operated on by an HIV positive surgeon : **SOME RISK**

Surgeons protect themselves and their patients by wearing gowns, masks and gloves. They do sometimes cut themselves while operating. However, the instinctive reaction to a cut is to withdraw and there is usually a pause before blood starts to flow, so the chance of dripping blood into a patient is very small. There is no known case as yet of a surgeon infecting a patient.

Being bitten by a mosquito : **NO RISK**

Although mosquitoes suck blood from humans, the quantity is very small and it is taken down into their stomachs which are acid. There would be too little virus, made largely inactive, to infect by the time the mosquito moved on to bite the next person. If mosquitoes (or any other insect) transmitted the virus, we would see a very different pattern of HIV infection.

Having unprotected vaginal sex : **HIGH RISK**

The virus could be present in semen, vaginal fluids or menstrual blood. Evidence suggests that women are twice as vulnerable to infection this way than men. This is probably because the vaginal walls are porous and it is common for there to be small 'erosions' on the cervix. Either of these could provide access for the virus into the bloodstream. A man is less likely to have cuts or sores on his penis. However, the risk of infection is increased if co-factors are present, such as genital ulceration, other STDs or a partner with AIDS. In all cases, use of condoms reduces the risk considerably.

Having unprotected anal sex : **HIGH RISK**

The virus could be present in semen or blood, and transmission could occur if the blood vessels in the anus were ruptured. They are very delicate and close to the surface, so this can happen easily. Again, the receptive partner is more vulnerable to infection, especially if co-factors are present. Extra strong condoms, designed for anal sex, used with plenty of water-based lubricant will reduce the risk somewhat, but they are still prone to bursting.

DISCUSSION POINTS Who has anal sex?

Having unprotected oral sex : **SOME RISK**

The virus could be present in semen, vaginal fluids or menstrual blood. There is a theoretical risk of transmission if a person has cuts or sores in their mouth, but there is no evidence of transmission this way, probably because there is likely to be a quantity of saliva present and we know that this will dilute and inactivate the virus. Using condoms or dental dams, avoiding semen in the mouth or contact with menstrual blood, will reduce the risk still further.

Masturbating : **NO RISK**

If it is done alone or to oneself, there cannot be any risk of infection. If a partner is masturbated, then care needs to be taken not to get semen or vaginal fluids into cuts or sores on the hands.

An HIV Positive mother : **SOME RISK**

Evidence suggests that an HIV positive mother is likely to pass her HIV antibodies on to her child before birth. This is part of the normal process by which a baby is given protection in the early months of life. In Europe less than 15% will also pass on the virus. A mother may have to wait until her baby is eighteen months old to know whether it is infected or not. There does seem to be a small risk of infection from breast milk, and in this country women who are HIV positive are being advised to bottle feed.

Who do you think should decide whether an HIV positive mother should have a child?

Is this an acceptable level of risk?

Eating food prepared by someone who is HIV positive : **NO RISK**

The only risk would be from blood, and people very rarely bleed into food. If the food is then cooked, the virus will be killed; if it is served directly, and the blood is not spotted by the person eating the food, then it will be diluted and inactivated by contact with saliva and gastric juices.

DISCUSSION POINTS How would you feel about eating in a restaurant where you knew the chef was HIV positive? Why do you think such strong emotions are aroused?

Working alongside someone with AIDS : **NO RISK**

With only a handful of exceptions, there is no risk of HIV infection from working alongside someone with AIDS. Even in these exceptional cases, the risk is more likely to be other dangers as a side effect of the illness eg a police officer not feeling she can entirely rely on her colleague with AIDS in an emergency, or someone whose brain is damaged as a result of HIV infection operating dangerous equipment.

4. **If a person is HIV antibody positive:**

Have they got AIDS? : **MAYBE**

A person may have HIV antibodies in their blood, hence they are 'HIV positive', but they may feel entirely well, and there may be no damage to the immune system as yet. Or they may have started to show signs of damaged immunity, and have been diagnosed as having AIDS.

Will they be dead in five years? : **MAYBE**

The progression of HIV varies enormously from person to person. Some people, who were diagnosed with HIV infection or AIDS ten years ago, are still alive and well, others have died very quickly after diagnosis. They could also be run over by a bus!

Is their sex life over? : **MAYBE**

It depends on the choices they make, and the kind of sexual activity they want. If they wish to protect themselves and potential partners, then unprotected vaginal or anal sex is not an option.

5. If you were worried about HIV or AIDS, and wanted information or a test, who would you talk to:

Your GP : **MAYBE**

If you have a good relationship with you GP then you may well choose to talk to her. However, there may be some problems: confidentiality is not always as good as it should be in GP practices; many GPs see very few people with HIV, so they may have little expertise and considerable fear or prejudice; and doctors are obliged to reveal medical information to insurance companies if they request it. If you want a test, the GP will probably refer you to the GUM clinic (see below).

An AIDS Helpline : **MAYBE**

They will provide accurate and up-to-date information and the opportunity for you to talk through you anxieties anonymously. They do not offer testing or treatment, however they will offer support and refer you to a clinic.

A teacher : **MAYBE**

If you have a sympathetic teacher who you feel you can talk to, this may well be appropriate. The teacher may want to involve someone else or refer you on, but they should not do so without your permission.

Your family : **MAYBE**

Again, this will depend on the nature of the relationship you have with them. Some parents will be more supportive than a young person believes; others may appear shocked or angered by unexpected questions or confidences, but with time will be extremely supportive.

Your friends : **MAYBE**

Certainly friends can be supportive and kind when you are worried about something, but they are generally not good sources of accurate and up-to-date information.

The GUM Clinic at your local hospital : **YES**

The service provided by your local GUM clinic is entirely confidential – its records are held quite separately from any other part of the health service, and information is not revealed to anyone. Here you can get advice, counselling, testing, support and treatment free, in confidence and without judgement.

••• *What is Safer Sex?*

A good warm up to this activity is to ask the students to take a pen and paper, and write down the first word they think of when you say 'safer sex'. It is likely that the overwhelming response will be 'condom'. You can then pose the question - is this the only form of safer sex available to us?

In Australia there is a preference for the term 'safe' because 'safer' might suggest 'even safer than safe'. In the UK there is a preference for the term 'safer' because it implies 'safer than not safe but not as safe as safest' !

PURPOSE To clarify what we mean by safer sex; to consider a range of safer sexual practices; to challenge the belief that sex has to mean penetration.

AGE GROUP 14 – 18

LEVEL Requires some trust to have been built up in the group.
Requires some pre-knowledge and understanding.

TIME NEEDED Minimum of 45 minutes. It would be possible to complete the exercise over two sessions, not too far apart, by breaking after Stage 6.

MATERIALS Postcards.

METHOD 1. Give out pens and a postcard to each student. Ask them to write legibly and briefly on the card a definition of the term 'safer sex'.

2. Then encourage them to mill around and read each other's cards. Allow a maximum of about five minutes for this.

3. Ask them to find one other person who has written something similar on their card. Go and sit down together.

4. Using a new card, negotiate a joint definition of safer sex.

5. Mill around again, reading people's cards. Attempt to find another pair who have something similar on their card. Go and sit down in a four.

6. This time, using flipchart paper, negotiate a definition that the foursome is happy with. It doesn't matter if they don't quite complete the task, so long as they jot down the main points.

7. Pin the flipcharted definitions up on a wall. Allow time for the group to read them.

8. Discuss —
   The common themes in the definitions.
   The differences between definitions.
   Is anything missing?
   Does it only cover HIV/AIDS? What about other STDs?
   Is unwanted pregnancy included?
   Are there gender differences in the definitions?
   Why 'safer' rather than 'safe'?

This leads well into the next exercise.

● ● ●

●●● *Safe or Not?*

PURPOSE To explore a range of sensual and sexual activities; to consider what we mean by sensual and sexual; to identify safer sex options.

AGE GROUP 14 – 18

LEVEL Requires some trust to have been built up in the group.
Requires some pre-knowledge and understanding.

TIME NEEDED Minimum of an hour, though it will depend on how much discussion is generated. It would be possible to complete the exercise over two or three sessions by breaking after Stage 4, 6 or 7.

MATERIALS A copy of the transmission diagram (see page 47).

METHOD 1. Explain that you are going to explore sensual and sexual activities that two people can enjoy together, and ask students to work in groups of four to six. They will need to sit round a table or on the floor.

2. Give each group a piece of flipchart paper and a thick felt tip pen.

3. Explain brainstorming (see page 12), and ask them to brainstorm all the sensual or sexual things they can think of that two people might enjoy doing together. Allow about five minutes for this.

4. Ask each group to pass their sheet on to another group. Have the new group read the brainstorm and check out any words they don't know.

5. Pin all the sheets on the wall and allow time for the groups to read them. Encourage questions about the meaning of words on the sheets.

6. Discuss –
Similarities across the sheets.
Differences in the sheets.
Is anything missing?
Is there an emphasis on the sensual or the sexual?
Can you make a distinction between sensual and sexual?
Can all these activities be enjoyed regardless of sexual orientation?

7. Have the small groups re-form with another group's flipchart paper. Using agreed symbols, ask them to indicate all the activities that could be classed as 'safer sex' and any activities they are not sure about. You may be able to move among the groups and help them classify some of those they are unsure of (the diagram on

page 47 may help here).

8. Pin the sheets up again, and bring the students back into the whole group. Have each group report back briefly, raising any questions or uncertainties for group discussion.

9. Discuss –

What does the group notice about the lists?

Does anything surprise them?

How do they feel about the range of safe options?

Why does safer sex so often seem to mean penetrative sex using condoms?

Why is penetrative sex so often seen as the goal?

Are there gender differences? What are these about?

Can two people be close without being sexually involved?

REVIEW   You might want to encourage some pair or small group work – in single sex groups? – or individual reflection time. The issues to focus on will be –

What did I learn from that exercise?

How do I feel about it?

Are there any other issues I want us to talk about?

Ensure that there is time for feedback from this if students want it.

3

'*My Mother Said...*'

WHAT I HAVE BEEN TAUGHT ABOUT MYSELF AND OTHER PEOPLE

INTRODUCTION

CLASSROOM ACTIVITIES

- · **Feeling Good About Myself**
- · **Messages, Messages**
- · **Valuing My Body, Valuing Me**
- · **Values, Achievements and Goals**
- · **Appreciations**

●●● *Introduction*

The first section of the handbook explored feelings, values, attitudes and beliefs about HIV and AIDS. The activities focused on issues 'out there', but sometimes the issues touch us very closely. Then, the way that we respond is much influenced by the pattern of interlocking messages that we have received since infancy – about ourselves, our roles and our relationships.

These messages have been internalised as a set of injunctions that form the basis of our beliefs, values, attitudes and behaviours towards ourselves and others. They are crucial to the decisions we make as adults. Fundamental to this is self esteem, which is the way that we feel about ourselves as people, the image we have of ourselves and the way we imagine other people view us. It includes our perception of the way we look, our personality, our skills and abilities. If we feel good about ourselves we will want to look after our bodies; we will recognise that we have valid needs of our own; and we will have respect for the needs and wants of others. Self esteem forms the basis of our ability to be assertive – to be clear about what we want, to ask for it, to negotiate and to keep ourselves safe.

This takes us into realms beyond the traditional bounds of sex education, into personal, social and health education, and on into the hidden curriculum of the school.

In the past schools re-inforced negative self-image. They punished rather than praised; they labelled more than half our children failures; they focused on mistakes in pieces of work; they valued conformity rather than individuality; and at their worst they ridiculed, put down or humiliated those who were different. There has been a change, but traces of the old ways have left their mark, and there are attempts in some quarters to return to 'old fashioned standards'. If we add to this the effect of home circumstances, where many children have experienced neglect or abuse, it is not surprising that many of us have a badly battered self esteem, find relationships with others hampered by injunctions, and are unable to make good decisions about sexual behaviour.

This section starts with some ideas for developing self esteem, and then moves on to address the messages we have received about self and others. It is an essential pre-requisite to successful work in the next section on skills. Students have a great number of questions and concerns, uncertainties and fears. We need to create a climate where these can be expressed, listened to with respect and discussed in a non-judgmental climate. As the teacher you will need to consider whether the atmosphere in the classroom, (and in the school), is such that students will be able to tackle safely such sensitive and personal concerns.

Cutlery-eating burglar sent back to jail after psychiatrists give all-clear

A man who compulsively eats his way through cutlery, and sometimes cleaning equipment, was yesterday jailed for four years after psychiatrists decided he was mentally fit.

Doctors fear Allison Johnson, who has had 30 operations to remove eating utensils from his stomach, will die in prison next year, where he has already spent 24 years of his life.

Mr Johnson, aged 47, who pleaded guilty at Lincoln Crown Court to two charges of aggravated burglary, still has eight forks and metal sections of a mop-head lodged in his stomach.

After reading psychiatric reports which said Mr Johnson was not mentally ill, Recorder Michael Lee, QC, rejected pleas from Adrian Robinson, defending, to allow Mr Johnson to live the rest of his life outside prison. Mr Johnson, described as an alcoholic, had a routine on being released from prison, where all cutlery is plastic, said Mr Robinson.

He went to a restaurant and ordered a slap-up meal. When the bill arrived and he was unable to pay, he told the owners to call the police. And he ate the cutlery in the meantime.

Mr Robinson said: "He is in pain and holds his stomach all the time. He finds it hard to eat and obviously has difficulty in going to the toilet. He has had about 30 operations to remove cutlery from his stomach. There have been more operations for things he has eaten while in Lincoln prison. He has been told by a consultant that if he has any more operations he is likely to die.

"He has also been told he has about a year to live. The cutlery swallowing and his inability to stay away from alcohol comes from his lack of self-esteem."

●●● *Feeling Good About Myself*

It is difficult to have a one-off lesson on building self esteem. It is part of a process which needs to be built in throughout a programme of work. Here are some ideas of activities that are good at the beginning or end of a session. It will be important that everyone listens and respects what is said. It is also important that you listen for and gently challenge 'self-made put downs' and qualifications, like –

'Oh, I can't do anything, you know me.'

'My ugly mouth.'

'I can't think of anything.'

'Well, I am sometimes quite good at...'

'I'll see if I can try to...'

Repeat the instruction, feed the student with a genuine appreciation or ask the student to repeat the sentence without the 'sometimes', 'quite' or 'try'.

PURPOSE To focus on self esteem, and to attempt to build it.

AGE GROUP 11 – 18

LEVEL Requires some trust to have been built up in the group.
Does not require any pre-knowledge or understanding.

TIME NEEDED 5 – 10 minutes at the start or finish of a session.

METHOD At the start of a session, have the group sitting in a circle and ask them in turn to say –

'One thing I really like about me is...'

'My favourite way to spend a Saturday is...'

'One good thing that happened to me since we last met was...'

'If I could be anywhere in the world right now with anyone I chose...' (tell the group where you would be, what you would be doing and who with).

Or at the end of a session, have the group sitting in a circle and ask them in turn to say –

'One thing I really enjoyed about this session was...'

'One thing I am taking away from this session is... (a thought, an idea, a question or a skill)'

'Something I am looking forward to this week...'

'Something I am going to do for me this week...'

Games are a good way of boosting self esteem too, so long as the emphasis is on having fun rather than on competition, winners and losers. There are many books available on games for the classroom (see Resources section). ●●●

● ● ● *Messages, Messages*

This exercise will need roughly equal numbers of male and female students or a single sex group.

PURPOSE To identify the 'messages' students have received; and to explore the ways in which they may affect their ability to make good decisions.

AGE GROUP 14 – 18

LEVEL Requires some trust to have been built up in the group.
Requires some pre-knowledge and understanding.

TIME NEEDED Minimum of 45 minutes, though this will depend on the number of sentence stems you give each group and the maturity and comfort of the group. It would be inadvisable to split this session.

METHOD 1. Explain the purpose of the exercise, and divide the class into single sex groups of five or six people, each with a large piece of paper and a felt tip pen.

2. Ask the female students to brainstorm (see page 12) 'messages' that girls/women receive about their role, using sentence stems to help them; and ask male students to brainstorm the 'messages' boys/men receive about theirs. Explain that 'messages' may come from parents in particular; from other relatives, siblings, friends and neighbours; from the media – TV, radio, magazines, newspapers, videos and books; or from school. Unspoken 'messages' can be as powerful as things which are spoken.

SUGGESTED SENTENCE STEMS

- Girls are......

- Women should......

- Men like women who.......

- Girls who......

- It's best if women......

- Boys are......

- Men should......

- Women like men who......

- Boys who.......

- It's best if men.......

---

3. When the groups have had time to complete the task, ask them to consider which of the 'messages' are relevant to them, which have a positive effect on their behaviour and which have a negative effect.

4. Suggest that students work alone to reflect on and note down –

The 'messages' they have received.

The 'messages' that have had a positive effect on behaviour.

The 'messages' that have had a negative effect on behaviour.

What would they need to change the negative 'messages' to if they were going to make good decisions about behaviour?

REVIEW   Students may wish to share some of their learning in the whole group or in twos and threes where they feel safe.

● ● ●

●●● *Valuing My Body, Valuing Me*

This exercise could be done in several ways – as a written exercise on a work sheet; as a drawn record on prepared sheet of pictures; as a completely free response to the questions, perhaps using large sheets of paper and coloured crayons or pens; or as a collage or collection of items which represents the way the student feels about his or her body.

PURPOSE   To help young people value their bodies, as part of valuing themselves.

AGE GROUP   11 – 18

LEVEL   Requires some trust to have been built up in the group.
Does not require any pre-knowledge or understanding.

TIME NEEDED   Minimum of 20 minutes, though this will depend how long the handout sheet is.

MATERIALS   Copies of handouts or worksheets.
Coloured pencils, crayons, felt tip pens, pictures, or objects (this will depend on how you organise the exercise).

METHOD   1. Explain the purpose of the exercise, and have the class working alone.

2. Give out prepared sheets explaining what is expected of students. Stress that this will be a record of how they feel today; it may not be how they felt in the past or will feel in the future.

REVIEW   On completion of the exercise, encourage students to review what they have produced. They might –
> Complete sentence stems (see page 39)
> Ask another student for their perceptions, and discuss similarities and differences.

In small groups, or in a whole group, discuss –
> Was the exercise was useful?
> What did it bring up?
> What did you learn from it?

●●●

● ● ● **VALUING ME VALUING MY BODY ACTIVITY**

What are my favourite parts of my body?

....

What are the parts of my body other people like best?

....

How would you describe your body? Is it more like ..... or .....?

A rock or water

Beer or champagne

Monday or Saturday

A cat or a dog

A potted plant or a long stemmed rose

A Rolls Royce or a mini

A cello or a flute

Silk or wool

● ● ● **Rank the following activities, putting the one you do most with your body first and the one you do least last –**

check it ☐   enjoy it ☐

forget about it ☐   admire it ☐

worry about it ☐   touch it ☐

display it ☐   smell it ☐

criticise it ☐   care for it ☐

use it ☐   look at it ☐

● ● ●

••• *Values, Achievements and Goals*

PURPOSE   To offer students an opportunity to consider what they value in their lives; to identify their achievements; and to explore possible goals for the future.

AGE GROUP   14 – 18

LEVEL   Requires some trust to have been built up in the group.
Requires some pre-knowledge and understanding.

TIME NEEDED   Minimum of 45 minutes. It is important to allow enough time for this exercise.

MATERIALS   Coloured pencils, crayons or felt tip pens.

METHOD   1. Provide places for each student to work in relative privacy. Give out large sheets of paper and make plenty of felt tip pens and coloured pencils or crayons available.

2. Explain that each student is going to produce a representation on paper of their life from the beginning to the point when they imagine it will end. For example, this could be in the form of a line across the centre of the sheet or in the form of a winding road or river.

3. They should mark on where they are now. Then to the left of that indicate, with drawings, symbols or words at the appropriate point time-wise –
    Any people in their lives that they value.
    Any things in their lives that they value.
    Any places in their lives that they value.
    Any significant events in their lives.
    Any personal achievements that they are proud of.
    To the right of where they are now, they should indicate at the appropriate point time-wise, anything they would like to achieve between now and death, either personally or professionally, public or private, realistic or idealistic, big or small.

4. Make clear that this piece of work is for them, and they will not be expected to share it with anyone else.

5. When everyone has had time to complete the task, ask them to focus particularly on the future, asking themselves –
    Which of the things I have indicated are the most important for me?
    What will I have to do to achieve it?
    What are the first steps towards achieving them?

You might want to suggest individuals make a contract (see page 15).

REVIEW Bring the class back together again. Either, invite comments on the exercise or do a round of 'What I learnt from doing that exercise was...'

● ● ●

●●● *Appreciations*

This is a very positive exercise to end with when a group has worked together for some time and there is a high level of trust and support.

PURPOSE   To offer an opportunity for students to appreciate others, and to receive appreciation from others.

AGE GROUP   11 – 18

LEVEL   Requires considerable trust to have been built up in the group.
Requires considerable knowledge and understanding of one another.

TIME NEEDED   Minimum of 20 minutes, depending on the size of group. It is important to allow enough time for this exercise.

MATERIALS   Coloured pencils, crayons and felt tip pens.

METHOD   1. Explain the purpose of the exercise. Give each person a large piece of paper and access to coloured pencils, crayons and felt tip pens.

2. Ask students to make a small drawing or representation of themselves in the centre of the paper and add their name (just in case it is not recognisable!). Place all the pieces of paper around the room – on the walls, on the floor or on desks or tables.

3. Encourage students to take a felt tip pen, move around each sheet in turn and write a positive appreciation of the person. Emphasise how important it is that it should be genuine and positive. It could be something about the way they look, something they have done or a characteristic that you like in them. Allow sufficient time for this; some people will work faster than others.

4. When everybody has finished, ask students to collect their own sheet and read the appreciations. They should identify one that is particularly significant for them – it may be surprising, touching, funny or hard to take on.

5. Then put the sheets carefully aside to take home. You may want to suggest that students find somewhere to put it where they will be unexpectedly reminded of their worth.

6. Bring the group into a circle – a hugging circle if they are prepared to do this – and ask each student to share one significant appreciation from their sheet.

4

'It Won't Happen To Me'

PROTECTING MYSELF AND OTHERS

INTRODUCTION

SOME INFORMATION ABOUT SEXUAL BEHAVIOUR

CLASSROOM ACTIVITIES

- **What Options Are There?**
- **What Do I Want?**
- **100 Ways with a Condom**
- **Assertive Through and Through**
- **Asserting Myself**

●●● *Introduction*

It has been noted earlier that many young people believe 'it will not happen to them'. Adults often work hard to persuade them that it might, whilst denying to themselves the reality of young people's experience (see page 7).

We hide behind medical or biological terminology and information, because we feel comfortable and safe using phrases like viruses, immune systems, modes of transmission, risk groups and body fluids. We argue that it might embarrass our students or their parents or other colleagues if we raise the issues young people want to discuss in language that they use among themselves. This argument is often used as a cover for our own discomfort and difficulty. Nor is it sufficient – or fair – to give the message 'just say no'.

Young people don't exchange body fluids – they have sex. Nor do they think of themselves 'potentially shuffling their genital material' which I am assured is the scientific definition of sex!

If you are going to help young people make good decisions about their sexual behaviour, the message needs to be geared to the lifestyle of the audience. You will need to be prepared to talk honestly and openly with them about sexual matters.

This section deals with making choices about sexual behaviour, helping young people be clear about what they want and the skills of negotiating assertively.

●●●

●●● Some Information About Sexual Behaviour

In a survey of 153 women carried out at a GUM clinic in London, it was found that –

- 40% of women patients never used condoms

- 24% did not use condoms with casual partners

- 66% had had unprotected penetrative sex in the last month, 83% with their partner, 24% outside their relationship

- 19% had partners who had sex outside the relationship

- 10% had regular anal sex and never used condoms

The researchers commented that –

It is trite to think that safe sex adoption is simply a question of will for many women. Sex is often a much more complex behaviour, affected by the extent to which women are empowered to negotiate their sex, and the costs to them of withholding such sex.

Source : 'Risk factors of female HIV seropositive patients attending the clinic for sexually transmitted diseases at St Mary's Hospital, London', International Journal of STDs and AIDS, 1990, 1(5), 328-329.

In a survey of 1,000 16-29 year old holiday makers carried out in Torbay, Devon, it was found that –

- 24% had sexual intercourse with a new partner while on holiday

- 7% had two or more partners

- 47% of male tourists who were engaged to be married had intercourse with two or more partners on holiday

- 59% did not use condoms

The researchers commented that –

As this key group of tourists feel that they behave differently when in the holiday resort, then HIV prevention messages in metropolitan and non-tourist areas will be of limited relevance to their non-practice of safer sex on holiday.

Source : 'Sex on Holiday : the HIV related sexual interaction of young tourists visiting Torbay', Nicholas Ford, Institute of Population Studies, University of Exeter, 1991

In a study of 16-24 year olds in the South West of England it was found that –

- 58% of 16 year old girls said they had had sexual intercourse

- only 40% had used condoms last time.

Source : 'The Socio-sexual Lifestyles of Young People in South West England', Nicholas Ford, SW Regional Health Authority, Bristol, 1991.

In a study of young people in schools in the south east of England –

- 22% of year 10 pupils were sexually active

- 34% of year 11 pupils were sexually active

- 10% never used condoms

- 17% of girls had asked their boyfriends to use condoms and they had refused.

Source : 'The HIV/AIDS Education and Young People Project : Report on Phase 1', Stephen Clift, David Stears et al, Centre for Health Education and Reasearch, Christ Church College, Canterbury.

For further research evidence of young people's sexual behaviour, in particular that of young women, you are recommended to obtain the *Women, Risk and AIDS Project Papers*, by Holland et al, (see Resources section).

••• *What Options Are There?*

This exercise follows on well from the 'What is Safer Sex' and 'Safe or Not' (see pages 70-73). The same methodology could also be used to explore drug use.

PURPOSE   To encourage students to look at a range of options for sexual behaviour including those with which s/he may not agree.

AGE GROUP   14 – 18

LEVEL   Requires some trust to have been built up in the group.
Requires some pre-knowledge and understanding.

TIME NEEDED   Minimum of 45 minutes, though this will depend on the number of groups which have to feed back. It would be possible to complete the exercise over two sessions, not too far apart, by breaking after Stage 3.

METHOD   1. Divide the class into five small groups, if possible of mixed gender. Give each group a piece of flipchart paper and a felt tip pen.

2. Allocate one of the following options to each group –
Not being sexually active at all.
Just kissing and holding hands.
Safe sensual/sexual activity without penetrative sex.
Penetrative sex using a condom every time.
Penetrative sex without using a condom.

3. Ask each group to list all the advantages and disadvantages of their specific option, for themselves and (if relevant) for a partner.

4. Have each small group report back to the whole class. You may choose to allow some challenge and debate at the end of each presentation.

5. As a follow-up you could give each person a list of the options and encourage them to make a personal list of the advantages and disadvantages for them.

This leads well into the next exercise which helps students to clarify what is right for them.

•••

••• *What Do I Want?*

For this exercise you will need a fairly high level of trust in the group, and a comfortable private place to work. Some teachers may be anxious about the explicit nature of the exercise, but it is designed only to use the material that students bring to it.

PURPOSE   To help validate the sexual decisions students have made, are in the process of making or will make in the future; and to encourage further thinking around them.

AGE GROUP   14 – 18

LEVEL   Requires a high level of trust in the group.
Requires considerable pre-knowledge and understanding.

TIME NEEDED   Minimum of 45 minutes. It is important to allow enough time for this exercise, and it would be inadvisable to split it between sessions.

MATERIALS   A copy of the relaxation exercise.
A copy of the guided fantasy.

METHOD   1. Explain to the group that you are going to invite them to go on a guided fantasy. It will start with a relaxation exercise and will then be an opportunity to let their imaginations go. They will not have to share the fantasy with anyone else.

2. Ask students to get into a comfortable position – this might be on the floor or on a chair – and to close their eyes.

3. Take them through a short breathing and relaxation exercise. The pace of this needs to be slow and gentle – time yourself by watching the breathing of the group.

4. When the group is ready read the guided fantasy – you may want to adapt it for the group you are working with. Speak in a slow, soft voice, but ensure that you can be heard clearly. There is a tendency for the pace to be too fast, so verge on giving longer than you think is necessary at each pause.

5. When the fantasy is finished and the students are ready, ask them to take a few minutes to write down any feelings, thoughts or issues that came up from it. Emphasise that this is purely for them.

REVIEW   Discuss with the group –

Their experience of the fantasy (without sharing the content)

Was it useful?

Did any issues come up that they would like the group to address further?

● ● ●

● ● ● RELAXATION EXERCISE

Place your hands flat on your abdomen with the tips of your middle fingers just touching. Breathe in deeply through your nose, taking the breath right down into your abdomen, and out through your mouth. If you are doing this right, you should feel your fingers pull apart as you breathe in, and come back together as you breathe out. Do this three times, in a slow rhythm, checking that the breath goes really deep. Keep this pattern of breathing going.

Starting with your feet, tense them up as tight as you can while you breathe in, let the muscles go as you breathe out.

Then move on slowly through each part of the body, reminding the group to tense up as they breathe in and to relax as they breathe out – legs, thighs, hands, arms, buttocks and genitals, stomach, back, shoulders, neck, head, face.

Take three more deep breaths, in through the nose and out through the mouth.

Check that you are relaxed all over. If not, repeat the tensing and relaxing on that part of the body.

GUIDED FANTASY

We are going to spend some time thinking about you and a special friend –
someone you enjoy spending time with, someone you find very attractive, someone
you like to be alone with. If you haven't got a special friend like this at the moment,
either imagine the person you would like as a special friend or imagine the sort of
person s/he would be.

Picture this person.....how do they look?......what do you like about them?.....what
do you enjoy doing together?......

Pause

Imagine you are alone with this person – you may be at home, out for a walk,
anywhere you choose as long as it is a good place to be.....you have plenty of
time......

Pause

You feel excited to be with them......have you thought whether you want to be
sexually involved or not?......think about it now......remember you have a whole
range of options......you can choose.....

Pause

Have you talked to your partner about your feelings?.....do you know what their
feelings are?......what does your partner want?.......have a conversation with them
about these things......really listen to what they are saying.....

Pause

Is there anything you could not tell them?.....is there anything you need to tell them
about your sexual history?.....remember, you care for them a lot....

Pause

Do you both want the same things?.....are there differences?.....how are you going
to handle any differences?.....have you really listened?....have they really listened to
you?.....

Pause

Is there anything else you need to say?

Pause

When you judge they have had enough time, change the tone of your voice to bring them out of the fantasy.

When you are ready, say goodbye to your special friend.....come back into this room (at school, college or wherever you are working), open your eyes, have a good stretch and sit up slowly.

••• *100 Ways With a Condom*

This is a good warm up activity with a group prepared to take risks and be a bit creative. It leads well into work about using condoms. It could be used equally effectively to introduce dental dams, which are available to protect women particularly during oral sex involving her genitals.

PURPOSE To enable students to handle condoms without embarrassment.

AGE GROUP 14 – 18

LEVEL Requires some trust to have been built up in the group.
Does not require any pre-knowledge or understanding.

TIME NEEDED 10 – 15 minutes as a warm up. Allow a little longer if it forms a session in itself.

MATERIALS Condoms.

METHOD 1. Have the group sitting in a circle, including you.

2. Start by telling them a story something like this –

SUGGESTED STORY

I was walking down a corridor at lunchtime today and something on the floor caught my eye. I put it in my pocket while I dealt with three Year Seven boys who were fooling about outside the Head's office, and I've only just remembered it (at this point get a single wrapped condom out of your pocket). I've never seen anything like this.... I wonder what it is.... I can feel something slipping about inside the wrapping....I'll open it....goodness, it's pink....very sticky....(smell it).....it smells rubbery....(stretch it)....very stretchy.....oh look, it unravels as well. It looks awfully useful.... I could use it as a..... plant waterer when I go on holiday. I would make a small hole in the end, fill it with water and suspend it over my most precious plants, so they don't dry out while I'm away.

---

3. Then turn to the person next to you and say 'What do you think you could use it for? Would you like to tell us?' and so on round the circle.

4. If the group gets into it, you could well do at least two rounds.

REVIEW Ask the group how they found the exercise?

Did anyone have difficulty thinking of creative uses?

Did anyone feel uncomfortable handling the condom?

Why might we feel uncomfortable?

How might we overcome discomfort?

You might go on to encourage the group to touch and play with condoms, or use the Condom Thoughts as a stimulus for discussion on page 99.

● ● ●

CONDOM THOUGHTS

Your rubber or mine?

WINNER of one of the main categories at this year's International Advertising Film Festival in Cannes was a controversial Spanish Ministry of Health commercial for the use of condoms from the agency Contrapunto. Set in a school gym, the advertisement shows a teacher confronting a class of teenagers with a condom he has found in their changing room. One by one the schoolchildren claim that it is theirs. The intensive television and poster campaign,which was aimed at 15-17 year olds, provoked fierce debate in the Spanish media with opponents even seeking the views of the Pope in support of their case. Advertising delegates applauded the commercial at Cannes but may have wondered how it would have fare in their own countries.

I am worried about contracting a venereal disease during sex. What should I do? Also, I suffer from premature ejaculation. Any suggestions? And finally, I would like to increase the size of my penis. What do you recommend? – J.W., New York, New York.

Here are the answers to your queries;

1. Wear a condom. 2. Wear two condoms. 3. Wear three condoms.

© LDA Yes, AIDS Again

••• Assertive Through and Through

This version of the exercise is used to develop sexual assertiveness, but the story could be adapted to explore assertiveness in relation to peer pressure and drug use.

PURPOSE To explore what assertive behaviour is, and how we can demonstrate assertiveness in our behaviour.

AGE GROUP 14 – 18 (younger, if the story is adapted to a non-sexual theme, such as taking a pair of shoes back to the shop or telling your best friend that you can't see her at the weekend.)

LEVEL Does not require high level of trust in group.
Does not require any pre-knowledge or understanding.

TIME NEEDED Minimum of an hour and a half. It would be possible to complete the exercise over two or three sessions, not too far apart, by breaking after Stage 3, 4 or 5.

MATERIALS A copy of the story.

METHOD 1. Explain to the class that you are going to explore assertive behaviour, and that first of all you are going to read a short story.

2. Ask them to form small groups of about three or four students, and ensure that each group has paper and a pen.

3. Read the story fairly slowly. Ask each group to jot down and discuss–
   What Mary did well.
   What Mary could have done differently.

You may need to re-read the story.

4. Take feedback from the groups, and pull out the characteristics of assertive behaviour –
   look at the person you are addressing
   stand firmly
   speak clearly
   know what you want
   state what you want
   stick with what you want.

5. Have the groups re-write the script with Mary behaving assertively.

6. Give them time to practise it, then ask each group in turn to enact their version in front of the class. Encourage supportive feedback from the audience on how assertively Mary came across – was there anything she could have done differently?

7. De-role characters at the end of each presentation (see page 13).

REVIEW Discuss with the class the elements of assertive behaviour and the difficulties of putting them into practice.
Are there situations where you would like to be assertive?
Have you tried being assertive?
What have the difficulties been?
What have you learnt today that might help you overcome them?
This could lead into the next exercise, either using their own situations or the suggested scenarios.

● ● ●

● ● ● STORY FOR ASSERTIVE THROUGH AND THROUGH

Mary had gone to the cinema with her boyfriend. The film was good and she had really enjoyed herself. Afterwards, as they walked home across the park, he stopped and kissed her on the lips. She didn't want to be kissed – she wasn't sure why. They carried on walking for a while. She wanted to say something, but didn't know how to. She looked down as she spoke....

'Uh, Peter, I think we should get home'.

'Yeah, sure, but let's have another kiss first'.

'I don't think we should.....'

She lets him kiss her again. She says quietly:

'Peter, I don't want you to kiss me'.

'Why not?'

'I don't know.....'

'Don't you like it?'

'No it's not that .....'

'What is it then? You liked it last time'.

'Who said I liked it last time?'

'Well, I thought you did because you didn't say anything'.

'Oh, don't let's argue over a kiss. Its not important'.

'Well, it's important to me'.

● ● ●

●●● *Asserting Myself*

It will be important that the students have learnt some theory about assertiveness and practised some of the skills in a general context before they explore sexual assertiveness. See the previous exercise and page 100-102 for references to books on assertiveness. This exercise could equally well be used to practise assertiveness skills related to drug use.

PURPOSE To practise the skills of assertiveness in the context of sexual behaviour.

AGE GROUP 14 – 18

LEVEL Requires some trust to have been built up in the group.
Requires some pre-knowledge and understanding.

TIME NEEDED Minimum of 45 minutes. It would be possible to complete the exercise over two sessions, not too far apart, by breaking after Stage 4.

MATERIALS Scenarios for the trios to work on, if they are not using their own situations from the previous exercise.

METHOD 1. Ask the students to select two other people to work with (if they are willing it may be helpful to have mixed groups). Have them sitting facing each other, as far as possible out of earshot of other groups.

2. Ask them to label themselves A, B and C. In the first round, A will practise being assertive; B will be the person A is being assertive to; and C will be the observer.

3. Give each of the A's a card with a brief scenario on, or ask A to share his or her own situation.

SUGGESTED SCENARIOS

• Your girl/boyfriend has just attempted to kiss you and you don't want to be kissed.

• You would like to go out with the girl/boy sitting opposite you.

• The manager of the shop where you work on Saturdays has just put his arm around you, and told you how cuddly you are. You didn't like it.

• A boy in the class has just said that girls who carry condoms are slags. You disagree.

continued overleaf

---

4. Suggest to the groups that they spend a few minutes considering –
   What gender the two people are.
   How well they know each other.
   Where they are.
   What has already been said and how has it been said.
   What does A want to say.
   How is B likely to respond.

5. Then encourage the groups to role play the situation – remind A not to get side-tracked, to stick to what s/he wants to say.

6. De-role A and B if using imaginary scenarios; de-role B only if using students' own scenarios.

REVIEW Discuss with the group –
   how successful were you in being assertive?
   what strategies were particularly helpful?
   could you apply them to situations in your life?
   is there any other help you would like?
The exercise can continue by rotating the roles, and giving B and C a turn to practise being assertive. If there is a high degree of safety in the group students may want to practise negotiating safer sex. This can be done using the same methodology.

'*They've Brought It on Themselves...*'

CHALLENGING PREJUDICE AND DISCRIMINATION

INTRODUCTION

CLASSROOM ACTIVITIES

●●● *Introduction*

Prejudice and discrimination are widespread in schools. Teachers have traditionally dealt with the more blatant forms of physical or verbal abuse, and in recent years many schools have taken seriously the issue of equal opportunities. However, the subject of prejudice and discrimination is not often formally addressed in the curriculum.

It is not easy to teach. Prejudice and discrimination do not fit neatly into any one curriculum area, and they involve teachers and students in discussion of very personal and sensitive feelings as well as politically complex issues of institutionalised discrimination and oppression.

An HIV/AIDS District Coordinator –
'We have no homosexual community here; you might try District 'x', they have a theatre.'

If, when teachers challenge prejudiced or discriminatory behaviour in the classroom or playground, they genuinely want to create a more caring and tolerant generation of young people, and if, when they support equal opportunities policies for their school, they genuinely want to see a more just society, then they will recognise the need to complement these moves with a curriculum which addresses prejudice and discrimination.

This section provides a framework and some exercises to explore the issues in the context of HIV and AIDS. It raises homophobia as a key issue, but also allows for exploration of racism, sexism, class, disability and drug use. Some teachers may be concerned about using homophobia as an example of the effect of prejudice and discrimination, in case this brings them into conflict with the law or with guidance issued by the Department for Education. There are two documents which worry teachers – Section 28 of the Local Government Act and Circular 11/87.

First it is important to clear up any confusion that remains about Section 28. This states that –

A local authority shall not –

1. Intentionally promote homosexuality or publish material with the intention of promoting homosexuality;

2. Promote the teaching in any maintained school of the acceptability of homosexuality as a pretended family relationship by the publication of such material or otherwise.

However, a statement issued by the Department of the Environment makes clear that this Act is not applicable to schools because governors, rather than the local authority, have control over what and how sex education is taught.

'My parents would excommunicate me if they found out that I was gay. My father says things like 'All gay people should be burned'.

Therefore teachers need only be concerned with the guidance given in Circular 11/87.

This advises teachers that –
"There is no place in any school in any circumstances for teaching which advocates homosexual behaviour, which presents it as the 'norm', or which encourages homosexual experimentation by pupils.....It must also be recognised that for many people, including members of various religious faiths, homosexual practice is not morally acceptable, and deep offence may be caused to them if the subject is not handled with sensitivity by teachers if discussed in the classroom."

Good sex education is not likely to advocate homosexual behaviour or encourage homosexual experimentation any more than it would advocate or encourage any other specific form of sexual expression. Assuming that 'norm' is used in it's scientific sense meaning 'standard' or, in this context 'what most people do', then accurate sex education will not suggest that homosexuality is the norm. No teacher I have ever worked with has doubted the need for a great deal of sensitivity when handling the issue in the classroom.

Therefore, this statement, taken alongside the more general statements quoted on pages 16-18, clearly indicates that general discussion of sexual orientation, homosexuality or homophobia is acceptable in the classroom, so long as it is undertaken with sensitivity.

'In the four years since I have been in my present school several students have come out to me. Each has suffered misery at the hands of an education system which continues to ignore and alienate some 10% of our students.'

Concern is often expressed that if a teacher talks positively about homosexuality or reassures a student that homosexual feelings are normal they will be in danger of 'making a vulnerable person gay'. There is no evidence that a person's sexual orientation can be influenced in this way. Open and honest discussion of homosexuality is far more likely to be a rare reassurance to those who are gay and to play its part in challenging prejudice and discrimination towards lesbians and gay men. ● ● ●

I know you get AIDS if you're a poofter, but what does prejudiced mean?

● ● ● *Story Lines*

PURPOSE   To explore attitudes towards HIV and AIDS.

AGE GROUP   11 – 18

LEVEL   Does not require high level of trust in group.
Does not require any pre-knowledge or understanding.

TIME NEEDED   Minimum of 45 minutes. It would be possible to complete the exercise over two sessions, not too far apart, by breaking after Stage 4.

MATERIALS   A tape recorder.
A prepared opening line for the story.

METHOD   1. Have the group sitting in a circle with a tape recorder in the middle.

2. Explain that you are going to start off a story about HIV/AIDS, and you will pass it on to the next person. They will add a few sentences to develop the story, and pass it on again. Any member of the group will have the right to miss a turn.

SUGGESTED OPENING STORY LINES

• Chris had AIDS and today had not been a good day......

• Mary was on her way home from the GUM clinic. How was she going to tell her partner......

• David had always thought it was something that happened to gays and drug addicts.....

• Emma wished she could get it together to ask her Mum about AIDS.....

• Jane and Sue were really worried – Jane had been unwell for some time and now it looked like she'd have to get tested......

---

3. Each time a new character is introduced the name will be written up on a board or a flipchart.

4. Stop the story when it has gone a couple of times round the group, or when the group chooses.

5. Play back the recorded story. Ask the group to listen for attitudes being expressed. Make a list of them.

REVIEW   Discuss with the group –

what were the assumptions that led to the attitudes?

which attitudes were positive and which negative?

what was the effect of the attitudes on others?

where do such attitudes come from?

how common are they?

could we live without making any assumptions?

This exercise leads well into 'Carpark', 'Who Gets the Treatment?' or 'Language Speaks' (see following pages).

● ● ●

●●● *Carpark*

This is called the carpark game because it needs a large space and was first used in a carpark! Here, it is used specifically to address issues related to HIV infection – sexual orientation, gender, race and drug use – but it could be adapted to explore other issues.

PURPOSE To explore the ways in which prejudice and discrimination affect options in everyday life.

AGE GROUP 14 – 18

LEVEL Requires some trust to have been built up in the group.
Requires some pre-knowledge and understanding.

TIME NEEDED Minimum of 30 – 45 minutes, though this will depend how big the group is and how willing students are to speak out in the processing. It is not possible to split this exercise over two sessions.

MATERIALS Role cards.
A copy of the statements.

METHOD 1. At one end of a large clear space ask students to form a line, as far as possible side by side and facing down the room.

2. Give each person a card on which is written a role. It is not necessary to give everybody a different role: it can be valuable to see how two people interpret the same role. Explain that they should not disclose what is on the card until the end of the exercise.

SUGGESTED ROLES

• A gay man who is HIV positive	• A lesbian woman
• A heterosexual married man	• An HIV positive pregnant married woman
• A single pregnant 16 year old	• A wealthy male occasional cocaine user
• A gay man with AIDS	• A female prostitute who is HIV positive
• A gay man	• A heterosexual married woman
• A female prostitute	• An HIV positive bisexual married man

---

3. Allow a few minutes for students to imagine themselves into the role – to consider how old they are, where they live, what kind of lifestyle they lead.

4. Explain that you are going to read out a list of statements (see page 113). If, in their role, they can answer 'yes' they take a small step forward. If, in their role, they answer 'no' they remain where they are. They must make a decision one way or the other.

5. Ask students to take two steps forward if, in their role, they feel good about themselves and their lives.

6. One by one, starting with the person at the front, ask students to declare their role and make one statement about their experience of the exercise.

7. De-role students (see page 13).

REVIEW   In plenary discuss with the group –

What were the restrictions imposed on them by their roles?

What factors influenced whether they stepped forward or not?

To what extent did their own stereotypes or prejudices influence the decisions they made?

What have they learnt about the effect of prejudice and discrimination on people who are HIV infected?

● ● ●

● ● ● STATEMENTS FOR CARPARK

Are you able to –

have a full social life?

tell people what you do for a living?

travel freely abroad?

obtain a mortgage?

be open about your sexual orientation?

take your partner home to meet the family?

work in a children's nursery?

have the sex you want when you want it?

kiss your partner in public?

make long term plans?

get medical help when you need it?

feel safe walking the streets after dark?

get sympathy from society if you need it?

expect sympathy from your family?

be honest with colleagues?

have security in your employment?

have children with a partner?

marry your partner?

expect to die where and as you would like?

● ● ●

••• *Who Gets The Treatment?*

This exercise was originally developed to be used with adults on training courses, but was later adapted for use in school settings.

PURPOSE To explore feelings and attitudes towards people with HIV infection; and, in the process, to identify some of our own prejudices and assumptions.

AGE GROUP 14 – 18

LEVEL Does not require a high level of trust to have been built up in the group. Requires no pre-knowledge and understanding.

TIME NEEDED Minimum of an hour. It is not possible to split this exercise between two sessions.

MATERIALS A copy of the scenario (see page 116).
Copies of the outline information (see page 118).
An envelope for each piece of additional information – there will need to be the same number of slips in each envelope as there are groups (see pages 118-121).
Copies of the complete information (see page 117).

METHOD 1. Explain the purpose of the exercise, and divide the students into groups of six.

2. Read the scenario out loud.

3. Explain that each group of six will be working quite independently on the same task. Five of them will be a team who have to make the decision about who will receive treatment. The sixth will act as observer.

4. Ask the groups to identify an observer. Gather the observers together for a briefing, out of earshot of the remaining students. Explain that their task is to listen carefully to the discussion and jot down any assumptions or prejudices that they hear expressed eg 'If she's unemployed, she can't be any use to society' or 'If he's gay, then he'll spread HIV to other people'.

5. Distribute copies of the outline information on the five patients to each group. Remind them that they may request a maximum of twelve additional further pieces of information at any time during the next 30 minutes. As they receive a new piece of information they should fill it in on their information sheets. You will need to give this information to a group without it being revealed to any other group (see Materials above).

6. At the end of 30 minutes stop the exercise wherever the groups have got to. Ask each individual to consider the following questions –

How do you feel now?
Did you censor any feelings or thoughts?
What assumptions are you aware you made?
Did you express any prejudices?

7. At the same time you may find it useful to gather the observers together to discuss the assumptions and prejudices they heard.

8. Invite the observers to feedback what they heard.

9. Either ask students to form sub-groups of three (including the observer) or remain in their sixes to discuss their responses to these questions in the light of the observer's feedback.

REVIEW Bring the group back together. Reveal all the information about the patients. Ask the group to consider whether their decision would be any different now. Allow 5 – 10 minutes for this.
Then discuss –

What criteria were used to make decisions?
To what extent did assumptions and prejudice influence decision making?
Does this happen in real life?
Is there any way to avoid it?
What have students learnt from the exercise?

● ● ●

● ● ● SCENARIO FOR WHO GETS THE TREATMENT?

There are five people with **AIDS** being treated in a hospital.

A new treatment is available, but it is expensive and in short supply.

There is only sufficient now to treat one person.

Those who are still fairly well are most likely to recover fully. Those who are very ill may benefit in the short term, but are unlikely to make a full recovery.

You are the team which has to make the decision – who is going to receive the treatment?

You will be given some information about the five people, and you may request a further twelve pieces of information.

You have half an hour to reach a decision.

● ● ● COMPLETE INFORMATION ON PATIENTS

	JENNY	WINSTON	TRACEY	RICHARD	TERRY
AGE	17	26	1	50	34
MODE OF TRANS-MISSION	Sex	IV Drug Use	Pre-Natally from Mother	Sex	Haemo-philiac
STATE OF HEALTH	Fairly Good	Good	Fairly Good	Fair	Poor
OCCUPATION	Prostitute	Nurse	None	MP Sponsors moves to help deprived/ disabled	Unemployed Chef
FAMILY SITUATION	Single parent/ one son/ pregnant	Supports dependent mother/ married	Adopted/ new parents knew she was HIV+	Divorced/ two children aged 13 and 17	Wife/three children aged 2,4 and 7
FINANCIAL POSITION	Poor/lives in council flat/on Social Security	Fairly good/ rents flat/ wife works	Well off/ parents are lawyers	OK/ supports children/ owns flat in London	OK/ wife a teacher/ live in staff house

●●● OUTLINE INFORMATION ON PATIENTS

	JENNY	WINSTON	TRACEY	RICHARD	TERRY
AGE	17	26	1	50	34
MODE OF TRANS-MISSION					
STATE OF HEALTH	Fairly Good	Good	Fairly Good	Fair	Poor
OCCUPATION					
FAMILY SITUATION					
FINANCIAL POSITION					

● ● ● ADDITIONAL INFORMATION ABOUT JENNY

MODE OF TRANSMISSION Sex	**OCCUPATION** Prostitute
FAMILY SITUATION Single parent/ one son/ pregnant	**FINANCIAL POSITION** Poor/ lives in council flat/ on Social Security

ADDITIONAL INFORMATION ABOUT WINSTON

MODE OF TRANSMISSION IV Drug Use	**OCCUPATION** Nurse
FAMILY SITUATION Supports dependent mother/ married	**FINANCIAL POSITION** Fairly good/ rents flat/ wife works

ADDITIONAL INFORMATION ABOUT TRACEY

MODE OF TRANSMISSION Pre-natally from Mother	**OCCUPATION** None
FAMILY SITUATION Adopted/ new parents knew she was HIV+	**FINANCIAL POSITION** Well off/ parents are lawyers

ADDITIONAL INFORMATION ABOUT RICHARD

MODE OF TRANSMISSION Sex	**OCCUPATION** MP sponsors moves to help deprived and disabled
FAMILY SITUATION Divorced/ two children aged 13 and 17	**FINANCIAL POSITION** OK/ supports children/ owns flat in London

ADDITIONAL INFORMATION ABOUT TERRY

MODE OF TRANSMISSION Haemophiliac	**OCCUPATION** Unemployed Chef
FAMILY SITUATION Wife/ three children aged 2,4 and 7	**FINANCIAL POSITION** OK/ wife a teacher/ live in staff house

● ● ●

●●● *Media Messages*

This is an energy-raising and enjoyable exercise with a serious purpose.

PURPOSE To raise awareness of the power of the media to influence 'knowledge' about HIV and AIDS.

AGE GROUP 14 – 18

LEVEL Requires some trust to have been built up in the group.
Requires some pre-knowledge and understanding.

TIME NEEDED Minimum of an hour and a half. It would be possible to complete the exercise over two sessions, not too far apart, by breaking after Stage 4.

MATERIALS Cards with subjects on.

METHOD 1. Invite students to form groups of three or four, and give each group a large piece of paper, a felt tip pen and a card with a subject on it.

2. Explain that each group is to write a popular press headline and introductory paragraph to an 'AIDS story' focusing on their subject. This will probably take about 15 minutes.

3. Pin the stories up on the wall and encourage the group to move round and read them.

SUGGESTED SUBJECTS
• A heterosexual male member of Parliament
• A baby girl
• A young female prostitute
• A 22 year old female pop star
• A 28 year old male footballer
• A gay man
• A 35 year old wife and mother
• A 25 year old heroin user

4. Have a whole class discussion, considering –

How much factual information is in the stories?
How much is sentimentality, judgement, prejudice or myth?

5. Ask students to return to their small group and re-write the stories avoiding sentimentality, judgement, prejudice or myth.

Students pin these versions up for the group to read.

REVIEW Bring the whole group back together to discuss –

Was it easy or difficult to write the popular press story?

Why do they think this was?

What is the appeal of the popular press?

Was it helpful to re-write the story?

How easy or difficult was it to remove the subjective material from the story?

Why was this?

What kinds of things might you look for in future when there is a media 'AIDS Story'.

As a follow-up to this exercise you might like to use recent 'AIDS Stories' in the press to discuss and analyse for hidden (and not so hidden) messages about HIV infection (see pages 124-126).

● ● ●

ICE STAR CURRY'S AIDS AGONY

Tragedy of an Olympic hero

Olympic ice skating idol John Curry has AIDS and is in constant agony.

As Linford Christie heroically won gold for Britain in the 100 metres last night, one of our greatest gold medallists was battling the disease with a true champion's courage.

"He's an unbelievably brave man fighting a terrible illness and refusing to be cowed by it," said one of the medical team treating him.

"He's kept his humour and his humanity."

John, 43, triumphed for Britain at the Innsbruck winter games in 1976 and became his sport's most famous star.

But the once super-fit athlete has lost weight dramatically and needs round-the-clock care.

Sex-mad sports star Magic caught Aids from call-girl

Sports superstar Magic Johnson caught the Aids virus from a prostitute, it was claimed yesterday.

The basketball player paid regular visits to the Texan call-girl Rhonda, said her friend Carol Davidson.

"I have a lot more sympathy for Rhonda than I do for Magic," said Miss Davidson. "She was a hard-working girl who used her looks to live the good life. She didn't rape him, he initiated sex,"

The 32-year-old Los Angeles Laker star was a notorious womaniser who refused to use condoms, it was claimed.

"He just couldn't get enough," said one conquest. "Magic was like a wildman. It's no shock to anyone who knows him that he's got Aids. He's been playing with fire."

Johnson's affair with hard-core porn film actress Heather Hunter almost prevented his marriage to long-time girlfriend Cookie.

"When she found out about Heather she hit the roof," said a friend. "But Magic was so bewitched by the porn star he couldn't stop seeing her." Several showbiz stars including singer Paula Abdul, actress Robin Givens and dancer Ola Ray, fear they may have caught the virus from Magic.

Tennis star Martina Navratilova also attacked the player, saying she was shocked by his promiscuity. "If it happened to a heterosexual woman who had been with 200 men they'd call her a whore," she said.

●●●

Every time a famous person dies from Aids something strange and confusing happens. He is turned into a hero. At the same time it is hoped that his death will remove the "stigma" from Aids.

But it is begining to look as though the condition, far from being a stigma, is a stigmata – a sign of holiness on the body of a saint. This is the case with the rock musician , Freddie Mercury.

The words of canonisation were uttered on TV by (as is now the custom) Mrs. Virginia Bottomley: "I do think the death of somebody who has been so admired and has been such a hero in some respects does have a very profound impact."

Freddie Mercury certainly does seem to have been a hero "in some respects". He lived a life of heroic pleasure, reckless priapism, risk and extravagance. A man who hires a "glamorous couple" to expose their bottoms to guests arriving at a party at the Garucho Club cannot have been all bad. Presumably this was the sort of thing Mrs. Bottomley had in mind.

There were some examples of his hospitality that took one back to much earlier times. For one party he hired girls as lift attendents adorned from head to foot only in gold body paint. On another occasion he engaged dwarfs bearing small bowls of cocaine to move among his guests. He also lived a life of awesome promiscuity, and wanted everyone around him to be "turned on" sexually by his presence.

Freddie's fortune for Aids battle

Freddie Mercury, the flamboyant rock star who died from Aids during the night, is believed to have bequeathed a huge part of his £25 million fortune to fighting the killer disease.

The singer, who only admitted he was suffering from Aids on Saturday, was visited by his parents, Jer and Momi Bulsara, a few hours before his death.

He died at his £5 million home in Kensington of bronchopneumonia brought on by the disease. A post-mortem examination is expected to take place, with a private cremation later in the week.

Until this weekend only his closest friends, including members of his rock group Queen and Elton John, had known the tragic secret. But pictures of the self-confessed bisexual had, in recent months, shown his increasingly frail condition.

The part-Persian youngster was educated at St Peter's boarding school in Bombay and remained a member of the select Parsee faith, which practises the religion Zorastrianism.

When his father was transferred to England, the family were moved to a house in Feltham, Middlesex.

He went to Ealing College of Art, graduating in 1969 with a diploma in graphic art. He sang with a number of pop groups before creating Queen with Brian May, Roger Taylor and John Deacon, giving their first concert in February 1971.

Mercury spoke about death in one of his last interviews, saying: "I don't really think about when I'm dead or how they are going to remember me. It's up to them. When I'm dead who cares?" He was always open about his bisexuality, but by the end described himself as lonely and bitter. "I don't have any real friends. People tell me they're friends, but there we are. I don't believe them." But he lavished money-no-object gifts on friends and lovers alike.

His parties went on for days. After Wembley in 1987 he hired a body painter from Germany and the "uniformed" bell boys were narked. He hired Concorde to fly friends over the Atlantic for a sky-high party.

He once said: "Success has brought me world idolisation and millions of pounds, but it's prevented me from having the one thing we all need – a loving, ongoing relationship. Love is Russian roulette for me."

The caring face of Virginia Bottomley, the Health Secretary, was in the news last week when she announced that she saw no point in quarantining people with HIV who have sexual intercourse but don't tell their partners about their condition. 'Punitive measures,' she said, 'will only drive the disease underground.' Then, in reference to the Birmingham case in which a man is alleged to have knowingly infected a number of women, Mrs. Bottomley solemnly remarked that this was a grim reminder of the risks to heterosexuals...' etc.

Mrs Bottomley, I fear, is suffering from a terminal case of muddle.

One wishes that the AIDS virus had started among Caucasian heterosexuals. Then the normal public health measures for a lethal, incurable and contagious disease could be taken.

As it is, the virus happened to surface in the homosexual community, whose activists have sold Mrs Bottomley and her predecessors the notion of protecting the sensibilities of the infected is more important than protecting the lives of the uninfected.

We now have the first politicised disease in history.

The truth is that while the cause of the AIDS disease is a virus, the cause of the AIDS epidemic is a lifestyle and lunatic social polices.

OPINION
AIDS: Let's be honest

The next stage of the Government's AIDS campaign will warn against brief sexual encounters and will be directed primarily towards those away from home either on holiday or on business.

Good medical advice. And good ethics, too. But is the issuing of such a warning the best way to fight this battle?

Or is it another example of the authorities' reluctance to focus on those groups most at risk – homosexual men and needle-sharing drug addicts?

It is true that, theoretically, everyone is vulnerable: viruses, including the AIDS causing HIV virus, do not discriminate.

But the reality is that Aids does not seem to threaten normal men and women who do not have sexual relations with anyone from the high risk groups

SENIOR health experts described the Birmingham Aids scare as ill-founded and irresponsible last night after it was revealed that the virus may not have been transmitted through normal heterosexual practices.

They said new evidence about alleged sexual techniques adopted by Roy Cornes, the 24 year old haemophiliac infected with HIV from contaminated blood, could provide vital clues to why he was particularly effective in spreading the virus.

Previously undisclosed details from two of Cornes's female partners – apparently ignored or kept secret or unknown to Birmingham doctors – cast doubt on claims that the case is the clearest example of the potential danger to heterosexuals from "straight" sex, not just to high risk groups such as homosexuals and drug users.

In a crucial development, as revealed in the News of the World today, one of his former female partners said Cornes "preferred" un-natural sex, while another was re-ported to have said it happened on one occasion. Cornes is suspected of infecting at least four women including Gina Allen, a 20 year-old who died from Aids last month.

●●● *Language Speaks*

PURPOSE   To explore the way in which attitudes are expressed in the language that people use; and to understand the way prejudice and discrimination are experienced by lesbians and gay men.

AGE GROUP   14 – 18

LEVEL   Requires some trust to have been built up in the group.
Does not require any pre-knowledge or understanding.

TIME NEEDED   Minimum of 45 minutes. It would be inadvisable to split this exercise between two sessions.

METHOD   1. Divide the class into groups of about five or six. Give each group a large sheet of paper and a felt tip pen. On half the sheets have the title 'Homosexuality' and on the other half 'Heterosexuality' (or whatever words are most appropriate for your group).

2. Ask them to brainstorm for 5 minutes (see page 12) all the words or short phrases they associate with the word at the top of the sheet.

3. Pin up the 'homosexual' sheets together and the 'heterosexual' sheets together. Gather the students around them. Compare the two sets of words first –
What are the differences between the two sets of words?
How many words are supportive or validating?
How many words are unsupportive or degrading?
Then focus on the 'homosexual' lists –
Which words are used by women and which by men?
How many of the words refer to women and how many to men?
Why might there be a difference?
How might you feel if you were targeted in this way?
If you felt this way, how might you behave initially?
In the long term, how might you survive, cope, resist?
What would help you survive?
Do you recognise any of this behaviour among people who are lesbian or gay?

REVIEW   It may be useful for students to go back into their small brainstorming groups to discuss personal responses to the exercise. It is possible that some guilt and negativity will be felt. You might do some attention-out activities (see page 15), then in the small groups or as a closing round, encourage thinking about how different the world would be if lesbian/gay oppression ended or what students can do differently as a result of their learning from the exercise. ●●●

6

'What Can I Do?'

SUPPORTING PEOPLE AFFECTED BY HIV AND AIDS

INTRODUCTION

LIVES OF PEOPLE AFFECTED BY HIV AND AIDS

CLASSROOM ACTIVITIES

- · Peter is HIV Positive
- · Feel, Think, Do
- · Feelings about Loss
- · Helping Others
- · Learning to Listen

●●● *Introduction*

This handbook would not be complete without addressing the needs of people directly affected by HIV and AIDS. Because young people want to distance themselves from AIDS by believing that it won't happen to them, they also believe that it doesn't happen to anyone they know. At the present time this may well be true, though it could also be that fear of stigmatisation and discrimination discourages people who are directly affected from sharing with and involving others.

More and more young people will know people who have HIV infection, their family or friends. They may also come across people who are worried that they may be infected, but dare not go for a test. A positive caring attitude will make it easier for those affected by HIV or AIDS to be open and to ask for help.

This section offers exercises which explore what it might be like to have HIV or AIDS; some strategies for dealing with loss; and how the ability of family and friends to offer support is influenced by their feelings, thoughts and behaviours. It goes on to build some fundamental listening skills. Again, the focus is HIV and AIDS, however the skills and the learning are transferable to a wide range of other situations young people may find themselves in.

●●●

●●● *Lives of People Affected by HIV and AIDS*

Jasmine is 23. She is recovering from heroin addiction and now lives and works in London and is applying to become an AIDS counsellor.

❝I was diagnosed HIV last June. For a while my own way of dealing with it was to carry on using (heroin) – and towards the end, quite heavily again. And then I realised that I was committing a slow form of suicide. By using I wasn't doing anything I could be doing to stay well. I could have chosen to die then, but I chose to live and to do everything in my power to live. So being HIV actually helped me, because it made made me take a long look at what I was doing and decide it was time to stop.

I started drinking and smoking dope when I was about 15. I was bulimic too...I tried to kill myself. I needed oblivion. At that time it was just too painful to be with myself. I took speed and magic mushrooms while I was doing my A levels, and I went on to heroin when I was 18. It took me off speed and also at that time I thought it was quite glamourous. I was fixing in pub toilets – I think that's when I got the virus. Then I took a one way ticket to New York, and on my second day there I met a guy and moved in with him in Harlem. He was a coke dealer. First I just used cocaine, then back to heroin, then injecting coke and heroin together...

While I was out there I heard I'd got a place at college. When I came back, I thought I had AIDS then – I had sores all over me, my glands were all swollen – I was a mess. I didn't use heroin again until the day before I went to college.

Right from the start there, I got into a relationship. I thought, 'With him I'll straighten myself out.' But we ran out of things to talk about! So we'd talk about 'What if I'm positive?' It was something dramatic to discuss, and it made us feel closer. God, how sick! So I went for a test, in May or June last year. I actually said to them, I don't want the results till after my exams – but they phoned me just before the exams started and said, 'Come in and get your results". And I was positive.

I took the exams while I was on heroin. I retook them in September. I finished my relationship – I found that incredibly painful. They say you need to hit a rock bottom to change and come off drugs, and that was it for me. I would wake up in the morning and start crying – because I could feel. Then I'd take heroin and it'd be OK again.

I began to go to Narcotics Anonymous meetings. I'd been to one a few years before, and I couldn't stand it – all these people seemed to get on with each other and to be happy, and I thought, God, I don't even fit in here! This time, it was very difficult at first. I'd use and go to meetings, or I'd go to meetings and then use. But then I put down the drug. It was because of the HIV. I knew if I carried on using I couldn't fight the illness. I realise now I have two illnesses – they are my drug addiction, and being HIV positive

They go hand in hand, staying off drugs and being HIV. They both mean you have to take a long look at yourself and how you want to live your life. I still have to work very hard on my addiction, but the HIV helps me stay clean. I know I can't control drugs, and if I go out and use – because I want oblivion – it could go on for a month, and I would have affected my immune system. And right now I do not want to die.

I'm doing all the right things. I go for regular check-ups – I'm very healthy. I eat three meals a day. I take vitamins and things like evening primrose oil. I see Shirin (Shirin Naidoo, a healer working with the Terence Higgins Trust) and my counsellor. I'm not in a relationship now, but that's not because I'm HIV positive. I've had a fling since I came off drugs – we used safe sex, and it was really good. I can get into negative stuff and think I've got to settle for *anyone* who would be prepared to have a relationship with me. But being HIV is just a facet of me which whoever I get into a relationship with is going to have to deal with.

There was somebody I was getting to know, and he said: 'I'm frightened, because what happens if I fall in love with you, and you die? I thought : 'How can you be so negative?' But obviously I wouldn't have unsafe sex. And I would not risk having a child, unless my diagnosis changed. I think of adopting, but I don't know that they'd even allow that. I do mind. I like children, I want to be able to have that option, and this disease has taken it away with me. But I don't really have anger with the virus now. I've got a lot of acceptance. I get more angry with the addiction – thinking, God, I've got to go to meetings all my life!

I get a lot of support – from Shirin, my counsellor, my friends and family, though when I told my mother, it was crass: 'Okay, my life's a mess, but I'm HIV – what can you expect? I did it to make her feel sorry for me. But my parents have really educated themselves about this, and they're into positive thinking, too. My brother was the hardest person to tell, because I thought how I'd feel if it was the other way round. It was painful. But now we joke about it – the virus jumping around on the toothpaste – because we both know you can't get it like that.❞

●●●

●●● *Lives of People Affected by HIV and AIDS*

Paul is 27. He and his boyfriend Gus share a council flat in London, and he is in the middle of a maths and computing degree course.

"I'm extremely well, and have been all along. The only sign of AIDS I have is the Karposi's Sarcoma (a skin cancer that often occurs with AIDS). I told my mum I'm going to end up looking like a leopard. When things worry me, I make a joke and it did worry me to start with. But then I realised that it's not doing me any harm, nor causing any pain, except to look ugly. And the patches haven't got any worse since I started on chemotherapy.

I did work for a bit in an escort agency, but I don't think I got the virus there. I'd spent some time in the States before that and I didn't exactly behave myself. At that time' a few years ago, there were odd rumours about this 'Gay Plague'. We thought it was hilarious – a big joke people had made up. Then I was diagnosed HIV three years ago. Only a couple of people had died here then. The test was available and I just decided I wanted to know. There was no counselling about then. I didn't understand about it and carried on as usual.

Than gradually there was more publicity. I started hearing about people dying. This was 1985-86. New York was chaos, San Francisco was chaos; all the bars were closing. I became aware that it was dangerous and not nice.

It still wasn't worrying me too much. The statistics were 50-50 for developing AIDS from HIV infection and I thought I was bound to be one of the 50 per cent who are all right, because I'd always been so healthy. Then the next year it went up to 80-20. I got a lesion on my ankle about a year ago. It looked like a mole. No one took any notice. Then it got bigger and I got another. They did a biopsy and I went on holiday. It ruined my holiday!

I came back, got the diagnosis, and I straight away who I was going to d who I wasn't. I phoned everyone, to get it over and done with in one go: 'Just to let you know I've been diagnosed as having full-blown AIDS.' I'm not subtle. Anyway, how do you explain in a nice way? There's no point in beating around the bush.

I've found peoples responses to be very good. Only two people have had adverse reactions – both are still on the gay scene and they don't want to know. It annoys me that anyone could be like that. A few straight people still think that you can get it from teaspoons, or that it's only the degenerates of society who get it. But most people don't patronise me. The attitude I like is what I get at the hospital: 'Oh dear we've got you here for another 24 hours!' That's perfect.

Of course it's part of my life now. You can guarantee that any conversation I have will have AIDS in it. But I've had support from every direction. Gus's parents, my parents, people at college, the doctors. After Christmas I went to see a counsellor and that helped a hell of a lot. Now I'm seeing a psychoanalyst, and we just hit it off straight away. She's only charging me a tenner. I've always set up a support system for myself. I like people and I'm selfish, in that I know where to get support if I ever want it. I've never been underground – I've always been out in the open. Everyone knows I'm gay and have known since I was 17.

I'd decided I'd like to go to college before I got the diagnosis. I'd left school at 16 and I decided I must do something using my brain. I got accepted and I was over the moon. My course is another thing that makes me want to live. It's a boost because it's something to aim for. It's very important, if you're faced with a possibly terminal disease, that you aim for things. I'd like to get my BSc and then get a decent job so I could live comfortably. Nothing more. I've got everything else – my relationship, my family, my dog and my cat, a nice flat. I've got everything I ever wanted, apart from enough money.

The first thing I wanted to hear was: How long? The first prognosis was 22 months, which would have meant next March. Well, if you think you're going to die next March, you will die next March. I just feel I can cope with it. I'm on AZT all the time, with no side-effects. No pain, no physical symptoms, no tiredness. I tried acupuncture, but that would have ment going macrobiotic and I found it too boring. I did a course of autogenic training: relaxing, becoming aware of your body, going through mind exercises. Whether it's doing any good or not, you *feel* so much better.

In a lot of respects it's made me a better person, a lot calmer. I can't wreck myself any more. I've got to be nicer to my own body. I used to drink a lot and I have used drugs – just about everything going. I was very promiscuous. I'd go out to clubs until four in the morning and I'd have sex with five or six different people in one night. You can only do that for so long because it's tiring! I don't think it's AIDS – it's age! I don't regret any of it, because it's all been fun. The escort agency wasn't fun. It was money. It was work. I decided it wasn't worth the hassle. It was depressing me so I stopped.

I don't sleep with anybody else besides Gus now. He is HIV too and very healthy. We use condoms and safe sex – it took some time to get used to it, but it's fine now. I've no intention of being monogamous for ever, because I don't believe in it. But I haven't got to the stage where I could sleep with someone else, because they must be told and I haven't got to the stage of knowing how you can chat them up and tell them. The day I do I will.

I'm not a religious person. Divinity was a lesson I bunked off at school. If you go into Buddhism, it's a lot of chanting – I couldn't see myself doing that without having hysterics. There's a hell of a lot of people who use the idea of God as a backstop. I use my family and friends for support all the time. Apart from that, I've always had the strongest will to be healthy. I don't like being ill. I refuse to be ill and I'm not."

● ● ● *Peter is HIV Positive*

PURPOSE To explore what happens to people when they face an enforced change; and the extent to which gains and losses can be recognised.

AGE GROUP 14 – 18

LEVEL Requires some trust to have been built up in the group.
Requires some pre-knowledge and understanding.

TIME NEEDED Minimum of an hour, preferably an hour and a half. It would be inadvisable to split this exercise between two sessions.

MATERIALS Copies of 'The Story of Peter' (see page 134).

METHOD 1. Have the students sitting where they can write easily, and ensure they have paper and a pen each.

2. Tell them that you are going to read out a story about a young man called Peter(see page 134). You want them to identify as far as they can with Peter. At various points in the story you will stop and ask the students to write down their responses to a question.

3. Read the story, stopping for students to respond in writing to the questions.

4. Divide the class into groups of four or five students, and give each student a copy of the story. Encourage them to share their responses to each question in turn, noting similarities and differences in responses.

5. Then give each group flipchart paper and a felt tip pen. Ask them to note down –
   Any real losses for Peter.
   Any fears associated with loss.
   Any gains there could be for him.
   What obstacles would have to be overcome?

6. Bring the whole group back together and share lists.

REVIEW Working individually, in pairs or in small groups, consider –
   What would be the most important losses for me if I was Peter?
   What would be the possible gains for me?
   What have I learnt about the way people may respond to HIV and AIDS?
Bring the whole group back to a closing circle to share one thing each of them has learnt about the way people may respond to HIV and AIDS. ● ● ●

● ● ● THE STORY OF PETER

Peter is 21 years old. He has had a pretty good life up to now – he did well at school, he has a good job, loads of friends, he is a talented sportsman and fairly good looking. He has been going out with Sue for a few months and he is very much in love with her.

But he has been thinking recently about his future – and his past. Until he met Sue (and a bit after) he had had lots of casual relationships. He is wondering whether he should have 'an AIDS test'.

Q. 1 How do you think he is feeling?

Q. 2 What might change in his life if he does have a test?

He decides to go for a test, and the nurse at the clinic discusses the possible consequences of having one – particularly what the implications might be if the test proved positive. However, his mind is made up to have the test, and he goes ahead with it. He must wait ten days for the result.

Q. 3 How do you think he feels during this period?

Q. 4 What thoughts might go through his mind?

He goes back to the clinic for the result and he is told it is positive.

Q. 5 What do you think he feels on hearing this news?

Q. 6 What might his first thoughts be?

After a couple of days he decides he must tell Sue about it.

Q. 7 What thoughts or feelings might he have as he makes this decision?

He decides to tell his parents too.

Q. 8 What thoughts or feelings might he have as he makes this decision?

After some months he gets very ill. He loses a lot of weight and becomes weak.

Q. 9 What might he be feeling now?

Q. 10 What will be important for him now?

● ● ●

●●● *Feel, Think, Do*

PURPOSE To enable students to experience the way that conflict between feelings and thoughts sometimes results in inappropriate action; and to help them to pull feelings and thoughts apart in order to act appropriately.

AGE GROUP 14 – 18

LEVEL Requires some trust to have been built up in the group.
Does not require any pre-knowledge or understanding.

TIME NEEDED Minimum of 30 – 45 minutes, if you only use one round of situations.

MATERIALS Situation cards.

METHOD 1. Explain the purpose of the exercise, and ask students to form groups of three or four.

2. Give out situation cards, one per group. You may choose to have all groups working on the same issue or you could rotate several issues round the groups.

POSSIBLE SITUATIONS

• Your form tutor tells the class that a student who has been off sick for some weeks is returning to school tomorrow, and he wants people to know that he has AIDS.

• You overhear a conversation between your mother and another parent in which they are discussing the 'fact' that somebody in your class is HIV positive.

• In a sex education lesson at school your teacher is discussing sexual orientation and the prejudice towards people who are gay. Somebody asks her if she is a lesbian, and she confirms that she is.

• Your best friend phones you one evening sounding very distressed, and asks you to go round. When you get there she tells you that she has just heard her older brother is dying with AIDS.

• Your boyfriend of three months says he has something he must tell you. He says he has just met up with his previous girlfriend and he discovered that she has been an IV drug user for years.

• Your father has recently returned from one of many overseas trips, and he has been quite unwell since. He and your mother now have separate bedrooms. Last night you started to watch a television programme about AIDS – he immediately got up, looking agitated, and left the room.

---

3. Have the person with the card read out the situation to their group, and ask each person in turn to say –

What they feel about the situation.

What they think about the situation.

What they would do or say.

Allow about 10 minutes for this. It may be helpful for you to move around the groups – they may have difficulty identifying and distinguishing feelings and thoughts.

4. Then ask the groups to identify how each of their responses would affect those involved (ie what message would they be giving); which response(s) does the group think was most positive; can they think of any more positive responses.

Allow about 10 minutes for this.

REVIEW   You may want to have a discussion of the learning at this stage and again at the end, or you may prefer to work through two or three situations and then review. Discuss with the whole group –

Thoughts and feelings about the exercise.

Learning from the exercise the need to acknowledge feeling, but not necessarily to act on the basis of it.

Situations in which the learning could be useful.

If you have time, introduce new situations to the groups.

● ● ●

••• *Feelings About Loss*

This is likely to be a highly sensitive exercise. It will need maturity and a safe atmosphere to work well. If it is possible to meet in a comfortable room, this will help.

PURPOSE
To help young people explore feelings about loss; and to identify with those affected by HIV infection.

AGE GROUP
14 – 18

LEVEL
Requires some trust to have been built up in the group.
Does not require any pre-knowledge or understanding.

TIME NEEDED
Minimum of 45 minutes. It would be inadvisable to split this exercise between two sessions.

METHOD
1. Explain that you are going to do an exercise about loss. Each student will need a piece of paper and a pen.

2. Ask them to get into a comfortable position and close their eyes. You may want to use a relaxation exercise at this point (see page 94). Otherwise, give them a minute or two to settle down and focus inwards on their breathing and their bodies.

3. When they are ready, invite them to think of a time, at least a couple of years back, when they lost something important to them or when a change – like moving house or school – was imposed on them. Emphasise that they should not choose anything too painful or difficult.

4. Encourage them to focus on this event –
What was it?
Where did it take place?
Who was involved?
How did you behave?

5. Ask them to recall the feelings they had at the time – to try to put words to those feelings. After a few minutes, have them open their eyes and write down the words on their piece of paper.

6. When they are ready, ask them to close their eyes again and go back to a 'significant' time after the event, maybe a couple of weeks or a month or so afterwards. Ask them to recall their feelings at this point, and put words to those

feelings. After a minute or two, have them write these words down.

7. Then close their eyes once more and think back on the event. Ask them to identify their feelings now, and put words to those feelings. Have them write these words down.

8. Ask students to call out the words they wrote down at each stage. Make three lists, using a flipchart or a blackboard.

9. When you have all three lists, discuss with the group –
  What do they notice about the lists?
  Which is longest?
  Which words are negative and which positive?
You will probably find that the first list is longer than the other two, and that the words start very negative and gradually become more positive. You can highlight the fact that loss is a process of change. At first people often find it distressing, but with time may come to accept and even welcome it.

10. Ask the group to identify anything that helped them to move from the feelings they had at the start to the feelings they had at the end. Write these up too.

REVIEW Look at this list together and consider –
  Whether these can be generalised to other losses?
  How might they help us to understand someone living with HIV?
  What could we offer to people who are living with HIV?

● ● ●

••• *Helping Others*

PURPOSE   To explore with a group ways of helping people, and the appropriateness of strategies in different situations.

AGE GROUP   11 – 18

LEVEL   Requires some trust to have been built up in the group.
Requires some pre-knowledge and understanding.

TIME NEEDED Minimum of an hour. It would be possible to complete the exercise over two sessions by breaking after Stage 7 or 8.

MATERIALS   Copies of 'Helping Others – Buddy' and 'Helping Others – Kathy' (see pages 141-142).
Copies of 'Model for Helping People' (see page 143).

METHOD   1. Divide the class into small groups. Give out a piece of flipchart paper and a felt tip pen to each group. Give half the groups 'Helping Others – Buddy' and the other half 'Helping Others – Kathy' (see pages 141-142).

2. Read out the scenario section to the class (this is the same on both sheets).

3. Ask each group to consider the questions on their sheet and write their responses on the flipchart paper. Allow about 10 – 15 minutes for this.

4. Come back into the whole group. Pin up the flipchart sheets, placing all the 'Buddy' responses together and all the 'Kathy' responses together.

5. First ask all the 'Buddies' to report back briefly. Compare the lists –
Where are the similarities?
Where are the differences?

6. Then ask all the 'Kathys' to report back briefly. Compare these lists in the same way.

7. Discuss with the group how closely the Buddy perception of Kathy's problem and needs matches with Kathy's perception.
Are there any differences?
Are these important?
What might happen if the buddy acts on his/her perception?
Is it important to know Kathy's perception?
How might s/he check out what Kathy's perception is?

8. Now make a list, using a flipchart or board, of all the strategies that have been suggested for helping Kathy.

9. Introduce the 'Model for Helping People' (see page 143). Explain the changing power relationship as you move through the helping strategies. Make clear that none is wrong. In fact, a good example of appropriate 'doing it for' is in the situation when a person's clothes catch fire – you do not stop to ask them how they feel, you smother them in a blanket or rug! However, most of us find the strategies in the bottom half of the model more familiar, easier and quicker to use than those in the top half. It may, therefore be worth giving some attention to the strategies in the top half of the model.

REVIEW Encourage students to consider –
  Occasions when they use each of the helping strategies.
  Occasions when it might be helpful to try different strategies.

● ● ●

SCENARIO

Kathy is 32 years old and she has AIDS. She lives in a small house on an estate with her children who are 12 and 8. A buddy (that's someone who befriends a person with AIDS) from the local AIDS Helpline visits at least once a week. Kathy says she is very worried that her little garden is such a mess. Over the years it has given her a great deal of pleasure, but now it seems too much. She sits looking out of the window at its overgrown state and feels depressed.

Questions

Imagine you are the buddy –

What do you think is worrying and depressing Kathy?

What do you think she wants from you?

● ● ●

SCENARIO

Kathy is 32 years old and she has AIDS. She lives in a small house on an estate with her children who are 12 and 8. A buddy (that's someone who befriends a person with AIDS) from the local AIDS Helpline visits at least once a week. Kathy says she is very worried that her little garden is such a mess. Over the years it has given her a great deal of pleasure, but now it seems too much. She sits looking out of the window at its overgrown state and feels depressed.

Questions

Imagine you are Kathy –

Why might you be feeling worried and depressed?

What do you want from your buddy?

● ● ●

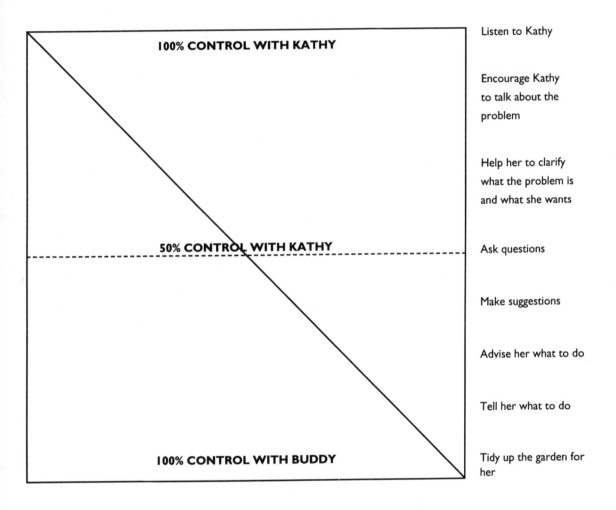

100% CONTROL WITH KATHY

50% CONTROL WITH KATHY

100% CONTROL WITH BUDDY

Listen to Kathy

Encourage Kathy
to talk about the
problem

Help her to clarify
what the problem is
and what she wants

Ask questions

Make suggestions

Advise her what to do

Tell her what to do

Tidy up the garden for
her

●●● *Learning to Listen*

PURPOSE To raise awareness of the value of listening, and to practise the skills.

AGE GROUP 11 – 18

LEVEL Requires some trust to have been built up in the group.
Does not require any pre-knowledge or understanding.

TIME NEEDED Minimum of 45 minutes. It would be inadvisable to split this exercise between two sessions.

MATERIALS Postcards.

METHOD 1. Explain the purpose of the exercise.

2. Get each person in the class to write on a postcard (or piece of paper) an issue that concerns them. It might be –
 A problem they have.
 A decision they have to make.
 A disagreement with a parent or friend.
 Something that makes them feel cross, upset or frightened.
 Something they feel passionately about.

3. Invite them to choose a partner to work with, label themselves A and B and arrange their chairs side by side. Ask A to talk for two minutes about their issue while B uses any strategy they can think of to avoid listening –
 Gaze out of the window
 Interrupt
 Start talking yourself
 Look at your watch

4. Ask the As how they felt –
 Were they able to talk freely and easily?
 What stopped them?

5. Now re-arrange the chairs so they are facing each other, and ask A to talk about their issue while B attempts to give really good attention.

6. Ask the As how they felt –
 Ask them what particular things helped?
 Did anything hinder?

144

7. Make a list of the things which helped.

8. Then ask them to pair up again with B talking for three minutes while A attempts to use all the listening strategies identified.

REVIEW   Discuss with the group –
   What they have learnt.
   What relevance does it have for their lives?
   Can they imagine ever using any of these strategies?

● ● ●

... Resources

USEFUL ADDRESSES

BACKGROUND READING ON HIV/AIDS AND RELATED ISSUES

TRAINING AND PREPARATION FOR THE TEACHER

MATERIALS FOR USE IN THE CLASSROOM

••• *Resources*

USEFUL ADDRESSES

AIDS Education and Research Trust (AVERT)
11 Denne Parade
Horsham
West Sussex RH12 1JD

0403-210202

Black HIV and AIDS Network (BHAN)
111 Devonport Road
London W12 8PB

081-742 9223

British Institute of Mental Handicap (BIMH)
Wolverhampton Road
Kidderminster
Worcestershire DY10 3PP

0562-850251

British Red Cross
National Headquarters
9 Grosvenor Crescent
London SW1X 7EJ

071-235 5454

Brook Advisory Centres
Education and Publications Unit
153A East Street
London SE17 2SD

071-708 1234

Catholic Marriage Advisory Council
Clitherow House
1 Blythe Mews
Blythe Road
London W14 0NW

071-371 1341

Daniels Publishing
38 Cambridge Place
Cambridge CB2 1NS

0223-467144

Family Planning Association (FPA)
Education and Training Department
27-35 Mortimer Street
London W1N 7RJ

071-636 7866

The Haemophilia Society
123 Westminster Bridge Road
London SE1 7HR

071-928 2020

Health Education Authority (HEA)
Hamilton House
Mabledon Place
London WC1H 9TX

071-383 3833

Health Education Board for Scotland
Woodburn House
Canaan Lane
Edinburgh EH10 4SG

031-447 8044

Health Promotion Agency for Northern Ireland
18 Ormeau Avenue
Belfast BT2 8HF

0232-311611

Health Promotion Wales
Ffynnon-las
Ilex Close
Ty Glas Avenue
Llanishen
Cardiff CF4 5DZ

0222-752222

Institute for the Study of Drug Dependence (ISDD)
1-4 Hatton Place
London EC1N 8ND

071-430 1991

Learning Development Aids (LDA)
Duke Street
Wisbech
Cambs PE13 2AE

0945-63441

National AIDS Helpline

0800-567123

National Children's Bureau
8 Wakley Street
London EC1V 7QE

071-278 9441

Sexual and Personal Relationships of the Disabled (SPOD)
286 Camden Road
London N7 0BJ

071-607 8851

Standing Conference on Drug Abuse (SCODA)
1-4 Hatton Place
London EC1N 8ND

071-430 2341

Teachers' Advisory Council on Alcohol and Drug Education (TACADE)
1 Hulme Place
The Crescent
Salford
Greater Manchester M5 4QA

061-745 8925

Terrence Higgins Trust
52-54 Grays Inn Road
London WC1X 8JU

071-831 0330 (admin)/071-242 1010 (helpline)

● ● ●

● ● ● **BACKGROUND READING ON HIV/AIDS AND RELATED ISSUES**

Adler, M. *ABC of AIDS*, British Medical Association, 1987

Aggleton, P. *AIDS : Scientific and Social Issues – A Resource for Health Educators*, Churchill Livingstone, 1989

Allen, I. *Education in Sex and Personal Relationships*, Policy Studies Institute, 1987

Conor, S. and Kingman, S. *The Search for the Virus: The Scientific Discovery of AIDS and the Quest for a Cure*, Penguin, 1989

Davidson, N. *Boys Will Be...? : Sex Education and Young Men*, Bedford Square Press, 1990

Frontliners. *Living With AIDS : A Guide to Survival by People Living with AIDS*, Frontliners, 1987

Gordon, P. and Mitchell, L. *Safer Sex : A New Look at Sexual Pleasure*, Faber and Faber, 1988

Holland, J., Ramazanoglu, C., Scott, S., Sharp, S. and Thomson, R. *Don't Die of Ignorance – I nearly died of embarrassment : Condoms in Context'*, The Tufnell Press, 1990

Holland, J., Ramazanoglu, C. and Scott, S. *Sex, Risk and Danger : AIDS Education Policy and Young Women's Sexuality*, The Tufnell Press, 1991

Miller, D. *Living With AIDS*, Macmillan, 1988

Morgan, D.(ed) *AIDS : A Challenge in Education*, Institute of Biology and Royal Society of Medicine, 1990

Richardson, D. *Women and the AIDS Crisis*, Pandora, (new edition)1989

Sarwar, G. *Sex Education : the Muslim Perspective*, Muslim Educational Trust (130 Stroud Green Road, London N4 3RZ), 1989

Sex Education Forum, *A Framework for School Sex Education*, Sex Education Forum (National Children's Bureau), 1992

● ● ●

● ● ● TRAINING AND PREPARATION FOR THE TEACHER

Aggleton, P. et al *Learning About AIDS*, Churchill Livingstone, 1989

Armstrong, E. and Gordon, P. *Sexualities : An Advanced Training Resource*, FPA, 1992

Brook Advisory Centres, *Confidentiality in Secondary Schools : Ethical and Legal Issues (England and Wales)*, Brook Advisory Centres, 1989

Clift, S. and Stears, D. *AIDS : the Secondary Scene*, AVERT, 1992

Department for Education, *HIV and AIDS : A Guide for the Education Service*, DFE, 1991

Department for Education, *Sex Education at School*, Circular 11/87, DFE, 1987

Dixon, H. and Gordon, P. *Working With Uncertainty : A Handbook for those involved in training on HIV and AIDS*, FPA, (new edition) 1990

Massey, D. *School Sex Education : Why, What and How*, FPA, (new edition) 1991

Munby, S. et al *Assessing and Recording Achievement*, Blackwell Education, 1989

National Curriculum Council, *Health Education* (Curriculum Document 5), NCC, 1990

Plant, S. and Stoate, P. *Loss and Change: Resources for use in a Personal and Social Education Programme*, Pergamon Education Productions, 1989

Rogers, R. (ed) *HIV and AIDS : What Every Tutor Needs To Know*, Longman, 1989

Sanders, P. and Farquhar, C. *Positively Primary*, AVERT, 1991

Taylor, B. *Experiential Learning : A Framework for Group Skills*, Oasis Publications (Beechwood Conference Centre, Leeds LS8 2LG), 1983

Townend, A. *Assertion Training : A Handbook for those involved in Training*, FPA, 1985

Whitehead, C. *Assertiveness Teaching Resource Pack*, Daniels Publishing, 1992

153

Books

Aggleton, P. Horsley, C. Warwick, I. and Wilton T. *AIDS : Working With Young People*, AVERT, 1990

Armstrong, E. *The Impact of AIDS*, Franklin Watts, 1990

BIMH, *AIDS : what it is and how to protect yourself*, BIMH, 1989

Brandes, D. *Gamesters 2*, Hutchinson, 1982

Brandes, D. and Phillips, H. *Gamesters Handbook*, Hutchinson, 1977

Canfield, J. and Wells, H. *100 Ways of Enhancing Self-Concept in the Classroom*, Prentice-Hall, 1976

Clarity Collective, *Taught Not Caught : Strategies for Sex Education*, LDA, (new edition) 1989

Dixon, H. *Chance to Choose : Sexuality and Relationships Education for People with Learning Difficulties*, LDA, (new edition) 1992

Health Education Authority *Teaching about HIV and AIDS*, HEA , (new edition) 1991

Sanders, P. and Swinden, L. *Knowing Me, Knowing You : Strategies for Sex Education in the Primary School*, LDA, 1990

Stanford, G. (British Edition Pam Stoate) *Developing Effective Classroom Groups : A Practical Guide for Teachers*, Acora Books (Oak House, Bishop Sutton, Bristol BS18 4UT), 1990

Ward, B. and Houghton, J. *Good Grief : Talking and Learning about Loss and Death* (for over 11s), Good Grief Associates, in association with Cruse, Cruse House,126 Sheen Road, Richmond, Surrey TW9 1UR), 1987

Kits and Packs

British Red Cross *Your Choice or Mine? Personal Relationships, HIV and AIDS*. Folens Publishers, 1991
Designed and field tested for use with 13 -17s, this pack which includes a video

is non-prescriptive, clear and accessible and provides a source of material which can be drawn on for a variety of sex, HIV and AIDS and relationship education courses in both formal and informal contexts. It is also a useful staff training tool particularly appropriate for those working in less formal settings.

Brook Advisory Centres *Penis Model Pack - Learning Strategies for Effective Condom Use*, Brook Advisory Centres, 1990
Intended for the teaching of effective condom use, the pack contains information, suggestions for discussion, photocopiable line drawings and an anatomically correct penis (without testicles) which is made of durable, white stone-like material to enable clear demonstration and practice.

Harvey, I. and Reiss, M. *AIDS Facts 4th Edition*, Daniels Publishing, 1992
60, A4 photocopy masters, spiral bound with a loose-leaf insert giving the latest UK HIV and AIDS statistics. Provides the relevant facts in a format that can be used by teachers or group leaders whether or not they have a biological background. Useful at Key Stages 3 and 4 and in Sixth Form.

Lothian Regional Council HIV/AIDS Education Project, *Choices - A Game About HIV and AIDS*, Lothian Regional Council (Community Education Service, Edinburgh), 1990
Pack includes 25 page handbook, question cards, 6 markers and a dice. Boardgame for use with groups of young people and an adult trainer/facilitator. It aims to raise awareness of issues of HIV and AIDS.

Manchester Health Promotion *Put Yourself in My Shoes*, Manchester Health Promotion Centre (Beech Mount, Harpurhey, Manchester M9 1XS), 1991
A simple card game for exploring issues around HIV and AIDS. It aims to encourage young people to see the world from other people's viewpoints through role play.

Riverside Health Authority *Opinions*, Riverside Health Authority (1st Floor, World's End Health Centre, 529 King's Road, London SW10 0UD), 1988 A boardgame with sheets of written cards, sheets of blank cards and a booklet with notes.
A non-competitive game for students 14 plus in groups of 3-8. Intended to reinforce information, encourage participation and initiate discussion. Could be easily adapted with visual symbols for use with those with reading difficulties.

Riverside Health Authority *Situations*, Riverside Health Authority (1st Floor, World's End Health Centre, 529 King's Road, London SW10 0UD), 1990
A game to explore choices and how HIV and AIDS might affect their lives. Requires trainer involvement and does not rely on reading skills.

White, M. *Self Esteem Set A and B : Its Meaning and Value in Schools*, Daniels Publishing, 1991 A4 photocopy masters
Set A explains how to introduce Circle Time into the primary or lower secondary school day. Aims to develop self worth. Set B encourages confidence and increases motivation.

Whitehead, C. *Assertiveness Teaching Resource Pack*, Daniels Publishing, 1992

Videos

Choices, Optima 1989
15 minute video drama for use with 14-18's. Follows the relationship between a young heterosexual couple as they struggle to communicate and face up to the issues of personal responsibility and safer sex. Includes teacher's notes covering the use of the video and 5 sessions on communication; responsibility; condoms; safer sex; HIV/AIDS.
Available from: Bloomsbury Health Education Department, St. Pancras Hospital, 4 St. Pancras Way, London NW1 0PE

Coming Soon, Central TV, 1987
All 5 programmes, (10 minute episodes) are based round a discussion in a Nottingham coffee bar between a culturally diverse group of young people. The discussion is broken up by information and anecdotes from experts and well known personalities. Following the arrival of a man with HIV and a woman with AIDS there is a stunning change of mood. Needs careful previewing in order to derive maximum benefit.
Available from: Academy Television (Thames), 104 Kirkstall Road, Leeds LS3 1JS

Danny's Big Night, Newsreel Collective for FPA, 1985
Encourages teenage boys to discuss how they see themselves in relation to each other and the opposite sex. Made before carrying condoms for safer sex equalled being sexually responsible, but still useful resource.
Available from: FPA, 27 - 35 Mortimer Street, London WIN 7RJ

AIDS : Sex, Lies and Stereotypes, Cambridge Video Unit, Works Theatre Company, Cambridge AIDS Programme, Cambridge University Students Union, 1990
A video to challenge young people to look at their sexual behaviour and how HIV and AIDS may affect their lives and relationships. Aimed primarily at Sixth Form and College students and comes with notes on how to use it.
Uses short dramatic scenes some funny, some serious to promote discussion. Some strong language is used.

Available from: Fiona Cameron, Bleaklow House, Howard Town Mills, Mill Street, Glossop, Derbyshire SK13 8PT

Leaflets/Booklets

A wide range of good leaflets are published by the following organisations :

AIDS Education and Research Trust

Brook Advisory Centres

Family Planning Association

Health Education Authority

Terrence Higgins Trust

● ● ●

Note: Some of the author's ideas developed in this book first appeared in *Working With Uncertainty*, published by the FPA and thanks are given to them for permission to reproduce.
Some of the activities in this book are adapted from *Taught not Caught*, published by LDA.